G000071341

The real name

of the man called Edward
in this book

was George Armitage.

He was a fine man
and a brave soldier.

PJ Campbell.

August 1979.

In the Cannon's Mouth

By the same author

THE EBB AND FLOW OF BATTLE

In the Cannon's Mouth

P. J. CAMPBELL

HAMISH HAMILTON
LONDON

First published in Great Britain 1979
by Hamish Hamilton Ltd, Garden House
57–59 Long Acre London WC2E 9JL

Copyright © 1979 by P. J. Campbell

British Library Cataloguing in Publication Data
Campbell, P J
    In the cannon's mouth.
    1. Ypres, 3d Battle of, 1917–Personal
    narratives
    I. Title
    940.4'31'0924   D542.Y72

    ISBN 0–241–10166–2

Printed in Great Britain by
Bristol Typesetting Co. Ltd, Barton Manor, Bristol

*To the memory of
all who lost their lives
in the battle of Passchendaele,
one of the most terrible battles in history,
those in our armies and in theirs.*

FOREWORD

I was nineteen and young for my years.

Today's more sophisticated young men may find it hard to believe that anyone could have been so immature as I was. But there were many like myself, products of a public school education and a middle class home. In fact, we were not altogether unlike themselves.

We had the same needs, physical and spiritual. We were in need of love and hope, laughter, occasional pleasure, affectionate comradeship always. This was what we needed, and what we were given.

May the young men of today be equally fortunate!

P.J.C.

CONTENTS

MAP

A*

1

The Sound of the Guns

The day came when I saw my name on the notice board by the Orderly Room of the Base Camp at Havre. A list was put up each day of the officers next to go. The typewritten sheet simply informed me of the number of the division to which I had been posted, the time of the train's departure, and the names of three other officers going with me. Redman and Trotford had been at Edinburgh with me and on the troopship that brought us from Southampton ten days earlier; and Manley I had got to know by sight in the camp.

Dick Adams also had been with me at Edinburgh and on the ship, and being young and full of hope we had considered the possibility of our going up to the line together. Dick was not only my greatest friend, he was unlike any friend I had ever had before. The short crossing to Havre had taken two days and three nights, owing to a report of mines, and we had carried our valises up to the top deck and unrolled them as close as we could put them. The wind was cold on deck, but our affection kept us warm and neither of us would have wished to be anywhere else. We were setting out together, knights in shining armour, on the Great Adventure. Lying under the stars, watching the lights of England slip away behind us I had no thought of fear in my heart in spite of the unknown that lay ahead.

I had ceased to pray, but the prayer I might have uttered was that Dick and I should be sent to the same division. That was my great hope.

But it was not to be. Dick had gone up before me and to a different division, I was going up with Manley instead. Redman, Trotford and I were newcomers to the War, but

1

Manley had been up before, he had been wounded in the fighting on the Somme last year and awarded the Military Cross. Now he was returning to the line.

Impressed by his experience and the ribbon on his tunic we three looked up to Manley, but his face was very different from Dick's and I did not like it.

Only a very little time was needed to show me that the face, not the ribbon, was the right criterion. He told us in the train on the following day that we should be sent to the Divisional Ammunition Column, not to one of the batteries. Newcomers always were, he said. Colonel Owen was the Column Commander and he was a holy terror to young officers. 'Especially to those,' he added, looking in my direction, 'who thought they knew everything because they had been to a Public School.' I had unwisely said something about what we did at Winchester. He told us anecdotes about the Colonel, what he had said to this subaltern, how he had threatened to court martial that one for some minor offence. Manley thought it very funny. 'Of course he wouldn't dare speak to me in that way,' he said, 'he knows I know more about the War than he does. He's never served in a battery.'

When he grew tired of trying to frighten us he started to tell stories of another kind. 'Heard the one about the tart who got up in the middle of the night to use her pot?' he began. I had heard it half a dozen times, but I had to listen to it again, and from one story he went on to another until he fell asleep. The train dragged its way through the night and I also fell asleep at last in spite of Manley's snoring and the ugliness of his open-mouthed face on the opposite seat. By this time the great adventure had lost its capital letters and my armour its lustre.

I woke with a jerk when the train stopped and saw that the others were already moving about in the carriage, collecting their kit. I heard a noise outside, but was so overcome with sleepiness that at first I did not realise what it was. Then I realised.

It was The Guns!

The sound was terrifying, more sinister than anything I had ever imagined.

I had to hurry, fearing that I should be left behind. We all

2

jumped down from the train. I saw that we were standing among the ruins of what had once been a village or small town. Hardly anything of it was left, just mounds of rubble, and one red brick wall ten or twelve feet high on which the name of the place—MIRAUMONT—had been painted in large black letters against a white background. A small clear stream was flowing beside the railway line, there were hills on each side, and it was from behind the hill across the railway that the terrible noise was coming.

The Sound of The Guns! It was a long way off, a continuous muttering. It seemed to have nothing to do with us. Here was a railway train and an engine letting off steam, here were soldiers, very many of them, washing in the stream, smoking, talking, standing about; over there was this terrible noise. No one seemed to be taking any notice of it, but that noise was the reason for our being here; we were going to the place where it came from.

If the noise had been nearer I might have been less frightened, or if we had been in any danger, or if any of the others had shown that they were listening to it. But I seemed to be the only one. I was afraid, my heart had failed, my courage had turned to water, but nobody else was paying any attention to the noise. I could hear nothing else, could think of nothing else. There seemed to be nothing else in the world, only that growling thunder, sometimes increasing in intensity, then falling away to a mere muttering until a sudden and louder crash reawoke the echoes to roll along the horizon.

The morning was bright, the sun was about to come up, but that sound took all beauty out of the light. It was a long way off, but it seemed the more menacing on that account. It was doing no harm to any of us, but its power to inflict evil seemed all the greater because it had not yet begun to inflict any.

We washed in the stream, bought cups of hot tea at the YMCA canteen, and breakfasted on buns and chocolate. Manley had found out where we were to go, and leaving our valises to be collected later we set out to walk the rest of the way, Manley, the two other officers and myself. The sun was well up in the sky by this time and the sound of the guns was less. One of the others commented on the comparative silence.

3

'Oh, that was the Morning Hate we heard,' Manley said. 'It's always like that at dawn.'

He was pleased to be back. He had been wounded not far from where we now were, but all the country over which we were walking had been behind the enemy lines at that time. Now the Germans had been driven back, Manley was elated and full of enthusiasm at the achievement. 'My God! It's wonderful,' he kept on saying. 'We've got the Hun on the run.'

All the villages had been destroyed, they were as flat as the little town we had first seen, and on both sides of the road the country was covered by shell holes. 'What a wonderful sight!' Manley said. 'I wish I could have seen it six months ago with the bodies of all the Huns. I bet our chaps enjoyed sticking bayonets into the filthy swine.'

There was a great deal to see as we walked along, but I could not take it in, my mind was stunned, my body was already tired, I saw nothing. We walked all day. First one way, then the other. Manley or the Railway Transport Officer had made a mistake. We went to the wrong place and had to return to Miraumont.

We rode in a wagon for the last hour or two, but it was late when at last we arrived at the headquarters of the divisional artillery. Manley went on to his old battery and I never saw him again. I was told to report to one of the sections of the ammunition column, as he had foretold.

I found my way to the officer's mess. They were having dinner when I reported, they had nearly finished, I was not made welcome. The dinner had been eaten, there was nothing left, it would be a trouble for the servants to start cooking again. Something was found for me to eat. Then where was I to sleep? There was another tent, but it would be a trouble to pitch it at this time of night. Someone suggested I should sleep in 'The Church' and the others agreed that this would be the best place. I wondered what 'The Church' was, but I did not mind where I slept. All I wanted was two yards of ground on which to unroll my valise which had come with us on the wagon. The church turned out to be some kind of tent, open at both ends and covered with a tarpaulin sheet.

When I had finished eating I listened to the others talking

4

and answered some questions about myself. I was not asked many, they were not interested in who I was or what I had done. I was glad when they said it was time to turn in and I could go to the church. I unrolled my valise on the ground, took off some of my clothes, and got inside the warm friendliness of my blankets. In spite of all my discouragement I fell asleep almost at once, but woke again after a few hours. It was raining. There were holes in the roof of the church and water was pouring down on to me. I moved my valise to another part and managed to find a place that was nearly dry, but I was cold and could not go to sleep again.

I dozed at last, but was roused into consciousness again by the sound I had heard in the early morning. The sound of The Guns! They had never been altogether silent, I had been aware of the noise ever since leaving the train, but for much of the day it had been spasmodic rather than continuous. It had seemed less evil and I had decided I might be able to learn to endure it. But the noise burst out again in all its fury and terrible power. It was nearer to me now. Through the open end of the tent I could see a red glare in the sky and red flashes stabbing the darkness.

Again my heart failed me, the noise was utterly terrifying. It was more than I could bear. I was still far away from danger. This was the sound of our own guns firing, but if I could not endure this what hope was there for me when I was in the middle of the fighting, and what would happen if I failed?

The year was 1917 and the month was May.

2

The Column

I became acquainted with Colonel Owen the first time I was
Orderly Officer. He came to Number Two Section looking
for trouble and found it. He saw a muddy horse rug lying
in the lines. I heard a great shouting and the words "Orderly
Officer", so I ran towards the noise and saluted the colonel.
He took a dislike to my appearance at once. Had I seen that
bloody rug? Had I found out whose it was? Had I put the man
under arrest? I should find myself under arrest if I went on
like this. If I thought he was going to allow his command, as
fine a unit as any in France, to lose its smartness, to be messed
about by a useless boy who looked as though he ought to be at
a girls' school—and would probably be no more use there—I
was bloody well mistaken. By God, he wasn't the man to
tolerate that sort of thing! He would make my life bloody
hell.

He succeeded in doing so at first. Every day he came to
inspect us and find fault. I was not always his victim, but often
I was. I knew very little about an officer's duties and never
learnt them while I was with the Column. Not one of the other
officers tried to help me, either with advice or with a friendly
word. They thought I was a prig, they may have been right,
but it was not from choice, I would not have been one if I
had known how not to be.

The morning was spent in the lines, the men at work,
cleaning something, harness, the mules, the camp, the officers
watching them and telling them to work harder. At some time
during the morning Captain Westerman, our Section Commander, came to inspect what they had done. He always said
it was not good enough and would have to be done again in

the afternoon. He was, I believe, a kindly man and left to himself would have treated us with consideration, but he was old, he had been brought out of retirement at the beginning of the War, he realised he was unfitted to hold any command, he was as frightened of the Colonel as we were and suffered from him more.

I was made to think that harness was what mattered most, having clean harness was going to win the war, but ours was never considered clean, however long the men were kept at work.

After tea, the Colonel found other occupations for his young officers. He made us attend what he called his riding school, or he or one of his staff gave us a lecture on the role of artillery in war. I heard one of the others say that the Colonel knew very little about any kind of war and nothing at all about this one, indeed that he had never been in action in his life.

While we were attending lectures, the men were set to work on making gardens. Gardens! This did astonish me. Nothing was ever planted in them, but the ground was dug and flower beds marked out with stones which then had to be painted. The gardens were outside the Colonel's headquarters and in full view of that part of the camp occupied by the General commanding the divisional artillery and his staff.

At the day's end the Colonel would sometimes come into our mess and laugh and make jokes, calling each of us his laddie and asking some pointless questions. We disliked him even more when he was pretending to be friendly than when he was abusive.

I heard the others talking about a probable move to a different part of the line. They said it would soon be time for us to start attacking again. They were right. After a week in this camp we moved up to Flanders. By ill chance it was my turn to be orderly officer on the day we left camp and marched to the entraining station. I was ignorant of most of the duties of an orderly officer and many of them were not carried out. The Colonel was beside himself with rage. One of our wagons overturned before we were out of the camp, and though this was not the fault of the orderly officer it was he who received

7

the blast of the Colonel's anger. Not only had he witnessed the mishap, but the General himself happened to be riding past at the time.

The General was waiting at a short distance from the camp to take the salute as we marched past him. Even I could see how ragged our marching was. I learnt afterwards that divisional ammunition columns were notoriously bad. Any battery commander having an officer, N.C.O. or man who he thought was no good sent him to the D.A.C. to get rid of him. This was what had happened in our division and I saw the result on this long day's march. Another wagon overturned soon after we had passed the General and the wheel of a third fell off. The Colonel and poor Captain Westerman rode up and down, cursing the officers, we cursed our men, the men kicked their mules, and the mules lay down whenever they got the chance.

Then the rain began. We were all wet through by the time we halted for the midday meal. The mules were watered and fed, the men were given their dinner, and then the officers went to get theirs on the lee side of the mess cart. I went with them, but was told at once of the things that the orderly officer had to attend to. There were so many that I got no dinner at all. One of the servants brought me a mug of rain and tea and I had some damp chocolate in my pocket. Then we went on.

The country through which we were marching was more desolate than anything I had ever imagined. It was last year's battlefield, the Somme battlefield. The war had passed over it and left it behind; there was nothing left but destruction. I saw no living thing off the road, and on it only our wet dispirited selves. The villages we passed through were so utterly destroyed that I should not have known we were in the middle of one if there had not been a board with the name of the place set up by the roadside. All the earth was shell holes, there was hardly a bit of ground that was not part of one, and because of the rain the holes were half full of water. There were no trees or flowers, only a little coarse grass in some places, and splintered stumps where woods had once been. Refuse was the only thing that grew there:

8

Cartridge cases and unexploded shells
Barbed wire
Empty tins
Vests and shirts and scraps of uniform
Picks and shovels
Rusty rifles
Broken and abandoned wagons
and
Wooden crosses.

Very many wooden crosses. Sometimes a man's name and his regiment were on the cross. Often just the words Unknown British Soldier, or unknown German one. Sometimes his helmet had been put on top of the cross, or his rifle had been stuck into the ground, muzzle downwards, above his feet.

Mile after mile was like this.

But the rain had one good result. The General rode away to get out of it, and when he had gone the Colonel and all his staff followed his example, and then poor Captain Westerman stopped nagging us and we left our men alone. In the late afternoon the rain stopped, the sun came out from behind the clouds, and in the same moment I realised that we had crossed over the battlefield and come through to the other side. I saw trees again, silver birches beside a lake, the sun shone on their wet trunks, and the young green leaves were shaking off their wetness. I saw children too, for we came to a village that was alive, not just a name on a board. Sunshine, trees, children. I was no longer afraid of going mad.

But the Colonel had not yet finished with us for that day. He sent for us in the middle of our evening meal. We were ordered to go to him at once. All the subalterns in the column were there, standing at attention in front of him. He shouted and stormed at us. He had never seen such march discipline. He was going to give us bloody hell. If we thought we could sit about on our arses all day . . . and go out whoring at night . . . by God we were mistaken! By God! . . . he was going to make us work for our pay. By God! . . . he would break some of us if anything like that happened again. We

9

were to learn 'Field Artillery Training' off by heart. Every word of it. That was our bloody bible, not a snivelling lot of Sunday School fairy tales.

He was drunk. Even I could guess what had happened. The General had sent for him before he sent for us, the General had told him what he thought about our marching, he had probably said a good deal about the Column and none of it complimentary. And the Colonel had come back to his own mess and had first tried to console himself with the whisky bottle, and then sent for us and was trying to forget his own smarts by making us suffer.

'Some of you lazy bastards will be wishing you'd never been born before I've done with you,' he said.

I could not help feeling a little frightened by his threats, he might be able to make our lives even more unpleasant than they already were, but the thought of what the General must have said to him gave me some satisfaction. I hated him as much as ever, but after that night I feared him less, I despised him.

3

Night Work

We saw much less of the Colonel in Flanders than before; our lives became easier instead of harder. There was real work for us to do, not just harness cleaning. Nearly every night I had to take ammunition up to one or other of the batteries in our division. It turned out to be less dangerous than I had expected. I had supposed that one was always under fire in the gun line, but night after night I went up and returned without having gained the experience for which I was fearfully waiting. I heard enemy shells bursting in the distance, and by this time I could distinguish the sound they made from the sound of our guns firing, but none ever fell near me. 'You're lucky,' someone at the battery would say to me perhaps, 'he was knocking hell out of the place half an hour ago, you've come just at the right time.'

Lucky? I supposed I was, but I wanted to find out what it was like, I could not enjoy being lucky until I knew what it was that I had escaped.

One thing that surprised me was the friendliness of all the officers I met in the batteries. I thought at first it must be that I had come across some exceptionally nice ones, but they were all the same. Then I learnt that it was the unfriendliness of the officers in the Column that was exceptional. In the fighting line everyone was friendly, but men in the Column lived a long way back, and where there was no danger there was no comradeship either.

All ammunition had to be taken up by night in Flanders. The enemy held the high ground and would have seen us by day. It might be all right for a single horseman, or two or three together, to ride along those roads, but not for half a dozen wagons of ammunition. I was always frightened of losing my way in the darkness, even though I had ridden along the same roads in daylight. Everything looked different at night and I had to make up my mind so quickly when I came to a turning, it might be the right one, but it might be only a track that led nowhere.

Once I got lost—in the middle of the village of Kemmel, hardly more than a mile behind the front line, underneath the long roof of the church, which looked all right in the darkness, but I had seen all the holes in it by day. I thought I was on a road, but it came to an end. We could not go on and we could not turn back, teams of six mules needed a lot of space in which to turn round. And I found there was only one wagon behind me, I had lost the other five. I was nearly in despair, I could see no way of extricating ourselves.

Then I heard voices in front of me and half a dozen soldiers came out of the darkness. I asked for their help. Between us we were able to turn the wagon round and I led it back to the road, where the other five were waiting for me. I never saw the faces of the men who had helped me, but I heard their Irish voices; they were like the voices of angels.

On another occasion I was too late when I arrived at the battery position. I had been up once already; this was our second journey that night, but we had been delayed and the officer at the battery told me that all the rest of their ammunition had been put away and camouflaged, tracks had been covered over, the men had gone to sleep. If he got them out and they had to do it all over again it would be daylight before they were finished.

So there was no help for it. I should have to take all my wagons back to the ammunition dump where they had been loaded up an hour or two earlier. One of them overturned in a ditch at the side of the road as we came away from the battery position.

The sergeant who was with me wanted to leave it there. He said it would be light before we got away, but I insisted on unloading the boxes of ammunition in the upset wagon. I sent the other five away, but the sergeant and I stayed. We took all the boxes out. Then when the wagon was empty, the mules were able to pull it back on to the road, and we put the boxes in again. This was not courage on my part, the sergeant was probably right. All the ammunition at the dump would not have been worth the life of one driver, but I had not yet learnt what was important, I had been given a job to do and it never occurred to me that it might be better not to do it.

Then we galloped along the road until we caught up the other five wagons. If the Colonel had seen us galloping I should certainly have been threatened with a court-martial, it was against all regulations, but I was slowly learning and one thing I had already learnt—that there was no chance whatever of my meeting the Colonel or the General or anyone who cared about my march discipline so near to the line when day was breaking. It was a very strong reason for preferring the vicinity of the line.

I was beginning almost to enjoy myself. I was lonely and had no friends; I was inexperienced and ignorant of an officer's duties; I never knew what mistake I should make next or who would have to pay for it, whether it would be myself or the men under me, yet youth was strong and happiness began to find a way through. If the night had gone well for us, if I had found all the right turnings, if none of our wagons had over-turned, or not more than one, if I had exchanged some friendly words with the officer at the battery taking my ammunition, if the night was fine, then as we were on our way back to camp I could not resist a feeling of satisfaction that was very close to happiness. Day was breaking, it would be quite light before we were back, I should find a meal waiting in my tent, there would almost certainly be letters for me including one from home. And then sleep. I should sleep for six or seven hours, hearing nothing, free of all anxiety.

That was on the way back from the line, but even on the way up, before difficulties or danger had begun, I was buoyed up by a feeling of expectancy, every sense was alert, the night stimulated me. I had seen the drab ugliness of war on our long

13

march in the rain, now for a few short weeks I lived in its Terrible Beauty.

There *was* beauty.

Even in Flanders, even so close to the line, there was early summer, there was the great vault of the sky over our heads, there were the stars. There were other stars, the German star shells, fired from their front line, shooting in an arch, and falling a mile or more from where we were, but burning with such a fierce bright intensity that all the countryside was lit up in silver—I saw the flat plain, the low willows bordering the dykes, the taller poplars, I saw their leaves shaking in the night breeze. Then the beautiful light went out, and it was so dark for a moment that I could not see the ears of the horse I was riding.

I made friends with the stars overhead, I had no other friends. They encouraged me, they seemed to talk to me. There was a ringing noise in the night, the Music of the Spheres. I had never heard it before and have never heard it since. The Milky Way lay above me and we were marching on another Milky Way. That was the name of the track leading towards most of the battery positions. I did not know why, probably because there was a tiny hamlet marked on the map as Millekruisse. It couldn't be chance, I thought; there must be a reason why two Milky Ways were so much bound up with my life, but whatever the reason I felt less lonely because of them, I felt a personal affection for the track along which we marched and for the galaxy of countless invisible stars over my head.

But I was still waiting to receive my baptism of fire. The others said they came under fire every night when they went up to the line. Either I was very unlucky, or they did not mean what I meant by coming under fire.

Then one night it happened. I had left camp at six o'clock with ten wagons, which were to be filled with stones at the railway station. Stones, not ammunition. I must have misunderstood my orders, for I thought I was to bring the stones back with me and that I should be back in camp in two or three hours. It was not until I arrived at the station that I learnt I was to take them up to the line, not up to the Kemmel area,

14

where the batteries were, but to a place on the other side of the village of Neuve Eglise. They were to be used for making a road across no-man's-land after our attack. I did not know Neuve Eglise, I had never been up to this area, but there was a guide to take me to the place.

We had a long march, but while the light lasted it was easy, and I had never been given a guide before, it made me feel free of all responsibility. But I was hungry. Thinking I should be back so soon I had brought no food with me. The guide said we were going too fast. We could not go beyond Neuve Eglise, he told me, until after dark because the road was under enemy observation. So we slowed down. I was in the habit of going as fast as I could, three miles an hour if possible. We were generally trying to make up for lost time because of some delay, but to-night the roads were emptier than usual.

We came to the first houses in the village. We passed the church. Now we were through the village and on the other side. It was not quite dark, I could see a little way in front of me and on either side of the road, but the guide said it was dark enough. This was the time I was so glad to have him with me, I needn't be straining my eyes all the time to see the road ahead. He was a soft-spoken countryman. His home was in Wiltshire, he told me; I found it easier to talk to him than to the men in the Column.

Now it was quite dark. The road was much worse. It was made of planks. I passed word back over my shoulder, warning the drivers to be careful their mules did not catch their feet between them and to beware of holes. I did not want to have an upset here. There was a smell of dead mules, I could see their bodies lying at the side of the road. Our mules were frightened and tried to shy away from the bodies. I could hear the drivers behind me cursing them, trying to hold them in.

Suddenly there was a noise in front of us, not very loud. It was like a train rushing towards us, or like the quick tearing of a huge sheet of linen. Then there was a red flash and an explosion. It was on our right, just off the road. Another and another. Then three more in quick succession.

So that was all. It hadn't been very frightening, the noise was not so loud as I had been expecting. It happened, and it

15

was all over. My heart was thumping a little, but I was conscious of a feeling of elation—I had come under fire, and it was all right, I could take it. We just went on, I wasn't going to admit to anyone that that was the first time I had been under fire. 'Nearly there now, Sir,' the guide said. Now I should have to take charge again and I alerted all my senses.

A man came towards us out of the darkness, peering at us. I told him I had ten wagons of stones. He led the first one away to the place where it was to be unloaded, I waited to count the others coming up. Two, three, four, five. Then no more. I could neither see nor hear anything.

'Where are the others?' I said to the drivers of the fifth team.

'Don't know, Sir,' was the reply I got. 'Lost touch with them after that shelling.'

What a fool I had been. Of course I ought to have ridden back immediately after the shelling to make sure that everything was all right at the rear of the column, instead of just marching on as though nothing had happened. I called for the guide; I would send him back to bring up the other wagons while I stayed to attend to the unloading of these. But there was no answer, the guide had gone. No one waited about when his job was done. Well, I should have to go myself. And I should have to be quick. I couldn't leave these wagons up here longer than was necessary.

I galloped back along the way we had come. Past the place where the shells had fallen, past the dead mules. I didn't think about holes between the planks or in the road. Nearly to Neuve Eglise. There was no sign of my wagons and I had seen no one to ask.

Then I heard someone riding slowly towards me and I drew up. We peered at each other. It was my sergeant. He had been riding at the rear of the convoy, and he told me that one of the shells had fallen on the road and wounded two drivers and all the mules in that team. But by the time he had come up the wagons in front were out of sight and he had to attend to the wounded men. He couldn't follow me with the other wagons, he didn't know the way; he had left the damaged one at the side of the road and taken the other four and the wounded men back to a place of safety on the far side of the village.

I told him to go back to them and wait there for me. I suppose I might have told him to bring them up to where we were, but I didn't think of it in time. Then I galloped back to where I had left the wagons unloading. I had ridden so fast that I arrived just as the last one had been emptied. I turned round, I took them back along the plank road. It was the fourth time that night I had ridden along it.

I had ridden fast, but half the night was over by the time we were all together again. Now what should I do? I could send my sergeant back with the five empty wagons while I took the four full ones up to the place where the others had been unloaded, but would there be time? Could I be sure of getting back here before daylight came? I looked at my watch again.

'What shall we do?' I said to the sergeant.

'It's up to you, Sir,' he replied. 'If you say to go up we'll go, we can leave the empty wagons to wait for us here.'

I thought I saw him looking in the direction of the eastern sky, I looked there myself. It was still dark, but I thought it was less dark than it had been, less dark there than in other parts of the sky, and the light came so quickly once it began to flow. I had noticed that on other mornings when we were returning from the line.

'We'd better go back to camp,' I said.

I was bitterly disappointed. The night had begun so well, but it had ended in failure. It seemed so difficult to carry out even a simple job like taking up ten wagon loads of stones to the line. But it was fully light, the sun had risen long before we were back in camp. I heard the larks singing and saw the Flemish farmers going out to begin their day's work. That was the strange thing about the war in Flanders, so short a distance separated peace from war. You could go up from the world of ordinary men and women, cattle and green fields, up into the very mouth of destruction, and back again to the same clean sights and smells and quiet noises, all in the space of a short summer night.

Perhaps I hadn't done so badly. Two of my drivers and

several mules had been wounded, but none seriously; I had lost a wagon, I didn't see how we could ever get that back; and I was returning with four wagons full of stones which ought to have been left up in the line, ready for road-making. But five loads had been taken there, and I had come under fire, and not been frightened by the experience.

'What's this I hear about your losing one of my wagons, laddie?' the Colonel said to me when he saw me in the camp later in the day. He was in his playful mood and he did not wait for an answer, nor say anything about the four that had come back full. I did not believe that even he could think it was worth going all the way to Neuve Eglise to bring back a damaged wagon.

A few nights later I had to go to the same place again with more stones. This time I was told to go a different way, a little further, but with more concealment from the enemy. It was one of the best nights I'd had. There was a full moon, I had no difficulty in finding my way, no shells fell near us, I took up my ten full wagons and brought them back empty. And I had eaten my supper and was in bed before three o'clock. But on the following night a man called Isaacs, an officer in one of the other sections of the Column, took up the stones. I knew he was going because I saw him in the camp not long before he set off and he asked me about the way. I told him what a good night we'd had, no difficulty, no shells at all, and he said he hoped he would be equally fortunate.

I was orderly officer the next day and had to get up for early morning parade. I was sharing a tent with Redman and when I returned to it I found him sitting up in bed, sipping the tea which our servant had just brought in.

'Heard about poor old Izzy?' he said.

'What about him?' I asked. There was a note of sympathy in his voice, which surprised me, for Isaacs was a Jew and was as friendless in the Column as I was myself.

'Gone west,' Redman said. 'Fini, napoo. Poor old Izzy!'

That was the way we talked in the Column, in order to show our familiarity with the expressions of front line soldiers, though afterwards when I was with front line soldiers I never heard one speak so unfeelingly about the death of a comrade.

18

Redman had just been told. They'd had a terrible trip, he said. Coal Boxes and Jack Johnsons all the way up. Izzy had been hit before they got there, and the wagons had turned round and come back. 'It's about time they stopped sending us out on that blasted stone fatigue,' Redman said. 'Poor old Izzy! He wasn't really a bad chap. There was really no harm in him, I mean.'

I sat down on my bed. This was our first death since I had been in the Column, and it was so unexpected. I had told him there was no danger, and he himself had said to me once that the only good thing about being in the Column was that it was less dangerous than in a battery. Did death always come when it was least expected? Redman said they'd had these big shells all the way up. I had experienced nothing of that sort, those shells on the plank road had sounded as though they could not kill anyone. Perhaps they had not been such big ones, perhaps I had not yet come under fire after all, not really. I should have to go through it again.

And I was sorry about Isaacs. He was not a friend of mine, but he had smiled at me once or twice. He had been smiling when I last saw him, as he said he hoped he would be equally fortunate.

4

C Battery

Then suddenly everything became different.

I had gone to our tent early on the previous evening. For once there had been no ammunition to take up and I knew our attack was being launched the next morning, the attack for which we had been brought up to Flanders, for which so much ammunition had been needed and the stones for road-making. The Column was under orders to move and the Colonel, to make sure that everyone had a tiring day, had ordered reveille to be at three o'clock. But I was awakened before then, long before daylight, by someone slapping the outside of the tent. A man came in and handed some orders to me. I rubbed myself awake enough to read them. I was to report at once to an Army Field Artillery Brigade and was given the map co-ordinates of its position. Would it be stones or ammunition I wondered, pulling my legs out of my sleeping bag. Nothing out of the ordinary anyway, I supposed. But Redman, who had taken the order from me, now explained. 'You're going away from the Column,' he said. 'You've been posted to this Army Brigade, whatever that means.' For a moment I was dismayed; I should be thankful to leave the Column, but it would mean another fresh start. There had been so many since I became a soldier and they had all been hard at first. I dressed and went out of the tent; I went to the latrine and I was there, sitting on the pole at Zero Hour, the moment when the artillery bombardment started and the infantry got ready for the assault. Books have said it was the greatest noise of the whole war, for a number of mines had been dug under the enemy front line and all were set off at the same moment. But I was so engrossed in my own concerns that I was hardly aware of the noise.

Then I set off just as day was breaking. An orderly was riding with me, he would take my horse back when I had arrived at my destination, I should have to make my own arrangements for collecting my kit at some later time. Everyone in the camp was up and about before I left, getting ready for the move, and I was aware of a feeling of great satisfaction that I should not be moving with them. The Colonel would have no difficulty in finding someone to curse, but it wouldn't be myself.

I said goodbye to Redman, but did not see any of the other officers. The Colonel and all his staff would be asleep still. He had an adjutant, an assistant adjutant, a medical officer, a padre and one or two others. The MO had once spoken a kind word to me, I had been badly bitten by a farm dog, he had cauterised the wound because of the risk of rabies, and had complimented me for not flinching. One kind word. None of the others, all living in comparative comfort and total safety behind the line, had ever noticed my existence. They had and have no share in the Brotherhood of fighting men, the fellowship of danger.

The place at which I had been told to report was four or five miles away, nearer to the front line, but still some way behind it. I noticed the beauty of wild roses growing in the Belgian hedgeside as I rode along and thought this was a good omen. They were the first wild flowers I had seen.

I found the place I had been told to come to, but could not report myself because no one was awake yet. This astonished me. In the Column there were always men awake and at work before six o'clock. I sat down on the ground to wait.

Presently I was joined by another officer who had come to report himself. His name was Vernon he told me, and his home was in South Africa. But he had been at school in England, he considered himself English and had therefore come back to join the British Army instead of enlisting in South Africa. I liked him, he was tall, fair-haired, nice-looking, he smiled a lot. There had been no-one like this in the Column.

21

I could talk to him. For the first time since leaving Havre I had a friend to talk to.

We spent all day together for Colonel Richardson, the commander of the army brigade, was in the line we were told. We should go there in the evening when the rations were taken up.

Vernon told me what an army brigade was. 'Like any other artillery brigade it consists of four batteries,' he said, 'but instead of staying always with the same division it is sent from one to another, wherever additional gun power is needed.'

He had been serving in a battery and was disappointed at being sent away from it. 'I hope to God they're not going to send us to an ammunition column,' he said, 'they're awful sinks.'

I told him I had been serving in one.

'Oh, bad luck!' he said. 'Was it awful?' 'Yes, it was. What's it like in a battery?' I asked. 'Oh, it's all right in a good battery. My battery was a good one. Most of them are.'

He was sorry to have been sent away, but the battery commander had been told to send one of his subalterns and he was the last to join. 'So it was only fair that I should go,' he said.

We spent the day at the wagon lines of the army brigade, where the horses stayed when the batteries were in action.

At last it was time for us to be driven up to Colonel Richardson. We were taken to a part of the line that was new to me, a few miles north of Kemmel, where most of my ammunition-carrying had been done.

We were directed to the Colonel's headquarters, a dark sandbagged dug-out. He looked different in every way from Colonel Owen. The first thing that struck me was the quietness of his voice. Colonel Owen had always been shouting. He was sitting at a table, looking at some papers, but he glanced up as we came in, and a captain sitting beside him smiled pleasantly. We saluted, told him our names, and said we had been sent to report to him.

'You've chosen a good time to report,' said the smiling captain, 'all our batteries are coming out of action tonight.'

The Colonel asked us a few questions, how old were we, how long had we been out. He made no comment, but said that I should go to C Battery, Vernon to B. Then he said that Captain Cecil, who was temporarily in command of C Battery, happened to be outside and would take me back with him.

Captain Cecil was a man of about thirty. He also asked me questions. 'First time out, is it?' he said. 'You'll have a great deal to learn, but I suppose you can learn.' He told me that the show, as he called it, had been a complete success, the infantry had gained all their objectives. The guns had been only two thousand yards from the line when the attack started, now they were out of range. 'But we've had the hell of a time in the last week,' he said, 'and a lot of casualties. Lieutenant Godwin was killed three days ago, I suppose you've been sent to take his place.'

Before we reached the battery he decided that there was no point in taking me with him because the guns were coming out of action that night. 'You may as well go back to the wagon lines, where you've come from,' he said, 'and report to Major Eric. He's the battery commander, I'm his second-in-command, I've come up because he's suffering from shell-shock.'

He asked me if I could find my way back, I was sure that I could, and this time I asked for C Battery lines and reported to an officer whom I found there. He was sitting without a coat, with the sleeves of his silk shirt rolled up, so I could not tell what his rank was. There was another officer with him, but I saluted the one without a coat and he acknowledged my salute. Again it was dinner time, as it had been when I arrived at the Column; again, the others had just finished their meal, but this time the coatless officer immediately called one of the servants and told him to bring me some dinner. 'What will you have to drink?' he asked. I was astonished, no-one had ever offered me a drink in the Column. If we wanted a drink in the Column we had to buy a bottle of our own and write our name on it.

He asked me where I had been at school and where my home was. He had been at Charterhouse, he told me. 'Damned good school,' he said. 'Brainy place too, though you might not think so from myself.' He talked about schools and universities while I was eating my dinner. He had been at Cambridge, he said, but they could only stick him for a year. Oxford was a good place too. Captain Cecil had been there and he had somehow managed to stay the course. He said nothing about the war or our attack or about the work I should have to do. He did not want to know about my experience or lack of it, but I put all this down to the fact that he was suffering from shell-shock, and therefore could take no interest in practical things. My valise and the rest of my kit had been left at the Column, but after dinner the Major ordered the battery mess-cart to be got ready and sent me back with it to collect all my things. I was away for three hours, but the guns had not yet arrived when I returned. They came soon afterwards. Everyone was tired, too tired to talk.

'Who's going to be Orderly Officer tomorrow?' Captain Cecil said. 'Who's had the easiest day? What time did you get up this morning?' he asked me.

'Half past one,' I told him.

'Whatever for?'

I could see he did not believe me and I did not want him to think me unwilling. 'But I had some sleep this afternoon,' I said.

'All right then,' he said, 'you'd better get up.'

Being Orderly Officer seemed not to make so much difference in a battery. I got up before the others and took the early parade before breakfast, and watched the horses being watered and fed, but after that there was nothing extra for me to do, and no-one found fault with me for what I had done or not done during the day.

Captain Cecil told me I should be in charge of the Left Section, the one Lieutenant Godwin had commanded. I had two guns and fifty horses and about the same number of men, gunners and drivers, under me. After breakfast he took me out with him and called up my two sergeants. Sergeant Denmark of F Sub-Section looked gruff, I thought; his look seemed to say that he was better fitted to command me than I to command him. But I liked Sergeant Feuerbach of E. Later in the day he gave me a Field Service Notebook in which he had written out the names of all the men in the battery,

24

those in the Right and Centre Sections as well as those in my own, and he told me something about every man in the Left. He told me that I had a good section, the worst he had to say of anyone in it was that he was a bit of a lead-swinger and needed watching.

I found afterwards that he was not popular in the battery. His German name had prevented his being sent home for a commission, and the men disliked his sarcastic tongue. I heard him using it sometimes, it was like a whip lash. But he was an extremely capable non-commissioned officer, and though his own good qualities were not always appreciated he was quick to see the good in others.

I asked him about harness cleaning. In the Column this had been the most important thing, and I thought that Captain Cecil or the Major or even Colonel Richardson himself might soon be coming to inspect it. But Sergeant Feuerbach told me there were no inspections of that sort in C Battery. 'If I see one of my drivers with dirty harness,' he said, 'then I let him feel the rough side of my tongue, unless I know he's been up to the line and has had no time to clean it. But when he cleans it, that's his affair, I leave it to him, that's the way we do things in C Battery.'

He told me that I had nothing to worry about in the Left Section. 'But all the battery is good, Sir,' he said. 'I don't believe there's a better one in France. Officers and men have always worked together, they trust one another, you'll never be let down by anyone in C Battery.'

I did not pay much attention to what he said about the goodness of the battery, supposing that everyone talked in that way about his own, as at school we had always said that our House was the best in the School and our School the best in the country. It would have been considered disloyal to say anything else. But I had never heard anyone in the Column speak like that, and looking at the smiling faces of my men, hearing their laughter as they worked, I thought that it might be a good battery and that there was a better chance of happiness for me now than there had been in the Column. Here I saw no sullen faces, heard no sound of angry shouting in the camp.

My horses also looked well cared for and contented. Those in my section were all bay coloured, reddish-brown with black manes and tails; the Centre were mostly chestnuts, the Right were blacks. I thought mine were much the most handsome, and my own charger, a big mare called Theodora, was the most beautiful of all. No officer in the Column had ever been given a horse like this.

The sunshine under the trees, the glossy coats of my horses, the happy-looking young men, many of them no older than myself, all these things combined to make me feel that my loneliness and unhappiness were over.

There were three other young subalterns in the battery, I was sharing a tent with two of them. They both went to sleep after lunch, and when I saw that there was nothing the Orderly Officer had to do I also lay down on my bed. When they woke up they began to talk and ask me questions. Frank was spectacled and intelligent-looking. He had already told me that he had been up at Oxford for two years and that the girl he was engaged to was at Cambridge reading Maths, and very clever. The fact that my home was in Oxford counted in my favour with him, he knew a number of people who were known to myself, we had already talked about them, he seemed very friendly. Jack was friendly too, he appeared to follow Frank's lead in everything. If I asked him a question he would suck at his pipe and watch the smoke coming out and then say 'What do you think, Frankie?'

Frank told me that I was lucky to have come to C Battery. It was the best battery in France, he said. It was a Yorkshire Territorial battery, Territorials were better than Kitchener-Army men and Yorkshiremen were better than any others, he said. The other three batteries in the brigade were not Territorials and they came from Lancashire, they were inferior in every way, although Colonel Richardson, himself a Lancashireman, and Captain Cherry, his adjutant, always favoured them. Yorkshiremen were better at everything, he said, fighting, cricket, making money, anything you like to mention. Frank was a Yorkshireman, Jack was not, but he agreed that there was nothing wrong with the battery. I learnt that the other officers also came from Yorkshire, and the fact that my grandparents had lived just inside the county and that I had walked on the moors, was a small point in my favour.

I said that I had been very impressed by what I had seen of the battery so far.

'So you should have been,' Frank said.

I said that Sergeant Feuerbach seemed very good.

'Sergeant Denmark is better,' Frank said.

I said that Captain Cecil seemed a very good officer.

'He's no good at all,'' Frank said.

I was silent for a moment. 'He told me what a bad time you'd been having,' I said.

'No worse than any other time,' Frank said. 'He thinks it was bad because it was his first time in the line during a battle, he doesn't know the first thing about battles.'

'It was quite bad,' Jack said. Don't forget about poor old Geoff.'

'I'm not forgetting. The fact that we had one officer killed doesn't make it the worst time we've ever had. Anyway, Cecil wasn't with us when Geoff was killed, the Major was still up in the line.'

I asked how the Major had been shell-shocked and they both laughed. 'You can call it that if you like,' Frank said, 'but other people might say it was too much whisky bottle.'

I told them about his generosity in offering me a drink, but Frank said I should find I was paying for it myself. The Major drank all the whisky, we paid for it in our mess bills, he said.

'I drink some of it,' Jack said, 'I'm not exactly a teetotaller.'

'He drinks more than all the rest of us put together, and then you've got to take into account what all his guests drink.'

Frank was annoyed at the mess bills being so big because he was saving up to get married. 'Not next leave, but perhaps the one after,' he had told me. He admitted that the Major was a good battery commander when he was sober. 'He has a good eye for a position and he chooses good N.C.O.'s' he said. 'The men like him and he leaves us alone, and you can trust him to find a good dug-out if there's one within a mile of us.'

He hoped the Major would be all right before we had to go back into the line. 'We've all had more than enough of

Captain Cecil,' he said. 'He's as much use as a sick headache in the line, he doesn't know the first thing about war. He's a proper wagon line hero. He's like you,' he said to me, 'he had spent all his life in an ammunition column until he came to us a few months ago.'

'I only spent a month in one,' I said.

'Did you ever hear the sound of a shell while you were there?'

I was foolish enough to tell them about the night at Neuve Eglise. Frank laughed in an unkind way. 'Wait till you've lived in the line for a month on end,' he said, 'and been shelled all day and all night all the time. Then you can talk about shellfire.'

Presently I asked about Edward, the third subaltern in the battery. Though I had seen him briefly, I had not yet spoken to him.

'He's all right,' said Frank shortly.

'He looks nice,' I said. In fact I had seldom seen anyone who had attracted me more at first sight. He had won the Military Cross. I had noticed the purple and white ribbon on the Major's tunic also when I saw him wearing it in the morning, but on Edward's ribbon there was a little rosette in the centre, which showed that he had won it twice. And he looked as young as or even younger than myself.

'He is nice,' said Frank, 'he's probably the best junior officer in the brigade, he's not afraid of anybody or anything, but if you want my advice I shouldn't take any liberties with him, not unless you want to get your head bitten off.'

'What sort of liberties?' I asked.

'Well, calling him by his Christian name for one thing, he keeps that for his friends.'

I had not intended calling him by his Christian name, but I did want his friendship.

We only stayed for a few days in the wood by the little stream, but instead of returning to the line we moved further away from it. I must have been the only person in the brigade who was disappointed at the direction in which we were going, everyone else was pleased at the prospect of spending another week or two out of action. There were inter-battery sports and football matches and parties in the evening, but I did not enjoy any of them. I wanted to go up to the line. I should not be accepted by the others until I had been in action with them.

Another officer joined us while we were out at rest. Pearson was his name, but all the others were calling him Josh before the end of his first day. He was as much of a newcomer as I was, he had not even been under shellfire once, he confessed to feeling afraid, and said he wasn't going to do anything more than he had to or put his nose outside a dug-out if he could help it. 'I'm not one of your heroes,' he said. But he was married and this seemed to be the reason for his quick acceptance. All the others were sure he would have something to tell them.

'What's it like, being married, Josh?' Jack asked.

'I expect you've had as much experience as I have,' was the reply.

'But marriage is different,' Jack said. 'Did you feel embarrassed on the first night? Do you undress her? How many times a night do you have it?'

Frank said he was disgusted by the questions. If anyone spoke to him like that when he was married he would punch them in the face.

But Josh did not mind, he said the young had got to find out these things, at school they were not taught any of the things that mattered.

The Major wanted to know how he had managed to avoid having children. Was it quite simple to arrange these things nowadays?

Josh said that he and Mary knew a thing or two.

Edward asked at what age he had begun.

'Not at your age,' Josh said. 'It's always the young that get into trouble.' Edward said he was older than he looked.

Frank said the conversation made him feel sick. None of us

seemed to know what love was. Jack said it was the only thing he did know.

Whatever they talked about, whether it was war or love-making I was left out. All the others were on Christian name terms with one another, but no one asked my Christian name. Frank snubbed me whenever I opened my mouth. Jack did not make unkind remarks, but he always agreed with Frank. Captain Cecil sometimes took my side in an argument because I was always willing to go and do a job in the horse lines, which the others were not; but his support did me no good with the others. He had served so long in a D.A.C. that he was considered almost as much of a newcomer to the war as I was. The others disregarded what he said, even his orders. Josh did not get up for early morning parade when it was his turn to be orderly officer and when I, thinking he had overslept, got up to waken him he was not at all grateful.

The Major talked to me; he would talk to anyone who would listen, officer or N.C.O. or man, all the officers in the brigade knew they could get a free drink by walking across to C Battery mess. It was no wonder that Frank worried about his mess bills. Edward, the one I most wanted for a friend, just ignored me. He may have had a particular reason for resentment against me. Geoffrey Godwin had been his friend, I had usurped the place that Geoffrey had once had, I was riding his horse, the beautiful Theodora, sleeping on his bed, sitting in his place in the mess. Frank scornful, Edward resentful, Josh mocking, I felt very much out on my own.

But I was beginning to understand. I was hardly more than a schoolboy in my thoughts and outlook. Colonel Owen had said I looked as though I ought to be at a girls' school and should not know what to do if I was there. It was true. I did not know. I knew as little about life as I still knew about the War. Josh knew about life, the others all knew about the War, they were men.

'It will be easier for us,' I said to Josh one day, 'when we've been up there and know what it's like.'

'Speak for yourself young fellow,' he answered sharply, 'I know when I'm well off and if you want to live to grow up take my advice and cut out all this silly schoolboy stuff about wanting to see the War. I can see it very nicely where I am, thank you.'

I did not want to see the War, but I did want to have friends, not to feel outside the battery ring. But I could not make Josh understand, he was already inside.

I should have to go through danger before I got there.

5

Preparing a Position

We left the pretty Belgian village with its hop-poles at last. Before the end of June the brigade was on its way back to the war. But we did not go into action at once. We were to prepare a battery position.

Now there was a lot of battle talk in the mess. I sat listening and did not interrupt. Never having taken part in one I could not imagine what battles were like and wanted to learn as much as I could before finding myself in the middle of one. Josh listened too; I could tell he did not like what he was hearing.

The Battle of Messines, the attack that had taken place on the day I came to the Battery, had been a complete success. But that had only been a beginning. The main battle was still to come. The enemy had been driven off the ridges from which he would have observed our preparations for the main battle, but that was all that had been achieved so far. It was going to be one of the biggest battles of the War. Most of the British Army seemed to have come up north, we were to break through the German line, liberate all western Flanders and clear the Belgian coast which harboured the U-boats.

'It will be a great thing if it comes off,' said Edward.

'If!' said Jack.

'It can't be a bigger fiasco than the Somme,' the Major said.

'I thought the Somme was a victory,' said Josh.

I also had thought so, but the others all laughed.

'You believed the newspapers,' Frank told him. 'You should never believe anything they say about the war.'

'It was a bloody awful defeat,' said Jack.

Edward would not agree that it was a defeat, we had achieved something, he said. But he admitted that our casualties had been appalling, he had been up at the Observation Post on the first day and had seen the slaughter.

'Whole battalions of the New Army wiped out without gaining a yard,' Frank said.

Josh was upset by so much talk about casualties, and when the others saw his apprehension they did their best to increase it.

'It will be worse this year,' Frank told him. 'They say the Boche has invented some new armour-piercing shell that goes through any dug-out.'

'There are no dug-outs up here,' Edward said, 'you come to water as soon as you start digging.'

'Cheer up, Josh!' said the Major. 'You may be one of the lucky ones, you may only lose an arm or a leg or some other interesting part.'

'I would rather be killed than have my matrimonial prospects blighted,' Jack said.

'I can't think why you ever came out,' said Edward. 'A married man of your age ought to have been able to work things.'

'Not so much about my age.' said Josh. 'How old do you think I am?'

'I don't suppose you'll see forty again,' Edward guessed.

'I'm thirty-two.'

'Well, that's quite a lot for out here, it's much worse for the elderly.'

'I could have wangled a job at home,' Josh said. 'I suppose I was a fool, but I thought it was nearly over, I had no idea it would be as bad as this.'

Again they all laughed. 'As bad as this!' said Frank. 'Why, you haven't been up to the line yet, you don't know what it's like.'

'Don't take any notice of them, Josh,' the Major said. They're all envious of you, they're such skinny things, they're much more likely than you are to get a bit of jagged steel in a vital part.'

33

But Josh clearly disliked the thought of getting a jagged bit of steel in any part of his body.

Jack went up to Potijze with a working party to prepare the new position. Sandbag shelters were to be made for officers and men, pits for the guns to give them some protection, and space found for all the ammunition to be taken up in advance and stored safely away.

A few days later Captain Cecil went to see how the work was progressing and he took me with him. I was very pleased to go, and to go with him rather than one of the others. Frank might say that Cecil did not know the first thing about war, but he knew a great deal more than I did and he enjoyed imparting information. We rode for two or three miles, then sent our horses back and walked the rest of the way. He asked me if I had ever been under fire. 'Only once,' I told him, 'and then it was only a few shells and only little ones.'

'Well, there won't be only a few today,' he said, 'and they won't be little ones either.'

He told me how to distinguish shells by the sound they made, and how to tell whether they were going to burst at a safe distance or not. 'When you hear a slow rather tired noise,' he said, 'you've got no need to worry, that one's not going to hurt you. But if it's a rumbling noise like this,' and he imitated the noise that a child makes, playing at trains by himself, 'then you run to the nearest dug-out. And if you hear a sudden whistling scream getting louder and louder and coming straight at you, then you fall flat on the ground and pray, you've no time for anything else.' And he told me always to keep an eye open for the nearest dug-out, so that I should know where to run to. 'Nobody minds your dropping in on them in such circumstances,' he said. 'They know it may be their turn to drop in on you next time.'

We were walking across a flat plain. In the distance, rather more than a mile away on our right, German shells were falling with steady regularity. Sometimes the black smoke of the bursting shell was mixed with red brick dust, showing that a house had been hit. 'That's Ypres,' Captain Cecil said briefly. I was excited at the thought that I was seeing Ypres. It was the most famous name of the War, and here I was within sight

34

of it! My brother had been killed in the first battle to which the town had given its name. Ypres! Now I really was at the front, I had seen Ypres, I had seen it being shelled. I could see some grey pinnacles rising out of the pall of smoke, like rocks out of the sea. Those must be the famous ruins, the Cloth Hall and the Cathedral. I should like to have stopped to watch, but Captain Cecil was hurrying on.

'That's a place to give a wide berth to,' he said. 'They never stop shelling it, they know that all our roads go through the town. Now we must walk quickly,' he presently added. We had been walking fast all the time and the morning was hot, I was sweating, I could hardly keep up with him. We came to a canal and crossed over it on a pontoon bridge. There was very little water in the canal, the bodies of horses and mules were sticking out of it above the surface, one could tell they had been dead for some time, but we stopped on the far side. 'There are good dug-outs on the canal bank,' Captain Cecil said. 'We can stop for a minute or two and get our second wind.'

A young and pleasant-looking gunner officer invited us in for a drink. I should like to have accepted; I was thirsty and hot, but Captain Cecil said we must go on. 'You don't want to stop even for a drink when it happens to be quiet,' he said after we had left him, 'because you never know when the Boche will start again, and we can get a drink from Jack when we're there unless he's finished it all.'

We were walking faster than ever and we seemed to be alone now. There had been men everywhere during the first part of our walk, men digging, filling sandbags, laying telephone lines, carrying heavy shells. But now there was hardly anyone to see. We were circling round the town, Ypres had been on our right at first, now it was behind us. We were crossing a maze of trenches, I could not have told where we were going, the shattered houses and sandbagged shelters all looked alike to me, but Captain Cecil never hesitated, though I knew he had only been up here once before. 'Come on!' he said, when I stumbled over some wire and stopped for an instant to push my helmet back away from my eyes. 'This isn't a place to loiter in,' he said.

35

We arrived. I wasn't sure whether to feel pleased or sorry that our journey had been so uneventful, we hadn't been under fire yet. We went round a wall of sandbags and into what had been a house, but instead of a roof there were more sandbags on top and bricks and broken rubble. It was so dark inside that for a moment I could not see anything. Then I saw Jack. He was only just awake, and was still lying on a bunk of wire netting. I knew that all work on the position had to be done by night.

'Got any whisky left?' was Cecil's first question.

Jack got up and lit a candle and poured some whisky into a mug for each of us, and filled it up with water.

'What's it been like?' Cecil asked when he had drunk about half of his.

'Not too bad,' Jack said.

I was looking at the dug-out. It looked rather comfortable, I thought. There were two bunks in it, one above the other, a small table and a chair, and some shelves had been cut into the walls. It was just high enough to stand up in, the ceiling was an arch of corrugated iron, strong enough to bear the weight of the stones and earth and sandbags on the top.

When we had finished our drinks we went outside, crossing over a road to reach the place where the work was being done. Jack showed Captain Cecil what they were doing and they discussed how much longer it would take. While we were standing there I heard a shell coming towards us, the others dropped to the ground, crouching behind a low wall, part of one of the unfinished shelters, and I followed their example. There was a loud explosion not very far from us, I saw the greyish-black smoke drifting away, smelled the bitter fumes of cordite, and heard the whine of bits of shell rushing through the air.

'That was a near one,' I heard a man say, and I felt grateful to him for making me feel I had got to the war at last. More shells followed, half a dozen in quick succession, but we were protected by the wall. Then we ran to a better place, but no one had been hurt. I was pleased to find that shells could fall quite near and yet cause no casualties.

Jack asked if we wanted to see the rest of the work that had been done, but Captain Cecil said we had seen enough, and the Major had told him to go and look at another position on the outskirts of the town, which we might have to occupy instead of this one. He wanted Jack to come with us.

We all three walked back along the road towards Ypres, but after a few hundred yards we left the road, crossing an area of rubble-strewn ground like that we had passed on our way up. But there were more houses here, or what had once been houses. None of them had roofs, there were holes in all the walls. Sometimes we were walking through a derelict garden, I saw flowers and over-grown bushes struggling against nettles and other coarse weeds. And in front of us, much nearer than before, I could see the famous ruins again, it looked as though my desire to enter Ypres was about to be gratified.

But the shelling began again, heavier than before, and louder, while we were still in the outskirts. We all ran. I saw the others dive through an entrance and followed them into almost total darkness.

'Come in, come in!' cried a cheerful voice. 'But shut the door behind you, don't let any of those big black bastards come in with you.'

Captain Cecil was apologising for the manner of our entry to an officer I could hardly see yet.

'Oh, don't mention it,' he said. 'We're accustomed to it, we keep open house here, we've still got some whisky left. Have some.'

We had some. When the noise outside seemed to have lessened I went slowly back to the doorway and looked out. No shells were falling close, the enemy had turned his attention to the canal bank, the place where we had been an hour or two earlier. From where I stood I could see all the bursts, some on this side of the canal, some on the other, one or two in the water. It was a spectacular sight, and since no one appeared to be in danger, at any rate there was no one in sight where the shells were falling and Captain Cecil had told me about the strength of the dug-outs on the near bank. I could give myself up to the enjoyment of it, as though I had paid for my ticket and was watching a military display. The shells were coming over at the rate of one a minute, I timed them with my watch. It was the ones that hit the water that were so spectacular. When this happened a great fountain of water leapt up into the air; I could see it splashing down on the bridges and the soft earth at the side. I wondered if one of the bridges would be hit, presumably this was what the enemy was trying to achieve; there were some near misses, but none was hit, and after about twenty minutes the shelling stopped and I rejoined the others, trying to give an impression that I had been with them all the time, for my newness to the war would certainly be shown up if it was known that I had gone outside to watch some shells falling.

'Well, we'd better be off while the going's good,' Captain Cecil said. Jack returned to where his men were, and we walked quickly down to the canal. 'What a place!' said Cecil. 'God help us if we have to take our guns to Dead End.' That was the name of the part of the town where we had been, because one branch of the canal came to a dead end there. He explained to me that you should always try to get out of the line in which enemy shells were falling because some might fall short, but if you moved to a flank you would be all right. 'The Boche never switches from side to side,' he said.

We recrossed the canal on the same bridge. Only a few yards from it on the far side there was a deep hole, which had not been there when we came up, in the middle of the track, and the lumps of darker earth lying round the edges of the crater had not yet been trodden into the ground. We walked very fast. It was not until we had left the canal about a mile behind us that Captain Cecil stopped and took off his steel helmet for a moment to wipe his forehead. He said we could relax now, we need not walk quite so fast. 'Well, how did you like your introduction to the war?' he asked.

I liked Captain Cecil. The others said he was no good, that he fussed about things which did not matter and knew nothing about those that did, but he was kind to me, looking after me like an elder brother, warning me how to take care of myself. And it was not only about the danger from shells that he warned me. As we left Ypres and the canal further behind us he began to talk on other matters. He advised me to change the bit on my mare's bridle. She had run away with me more than once and I had fallen off. A snaffle was not strong enough to hold her, he said. And he told me what a good time I should have when I went up to Oxford after the War. He had belonged to the Bullingdon, he said, and had ridden in quite a few point-to-points. 'I didn't do any work,' he said. 'Nobody does, only a few swots.' 'Frank told me that he used to work quite hard,' I said. 'Oh, he would!' said Captain Cecil.

That night, we all went to have dinner at the famous restaurant in Poperinghe, ten miles behind the line. The little town was full of shops and civilians, and soldiers briefly escaping from the war. I could enjoy it now. The glittering lights in the restaurant, the laughter and noise all round me, the good food and the wine, the pretty Belgian girl waiting at our table and smiling on us. I was elated, but it wasn't the champagne that had gone to my head. I had been under fire, it was all right, I hadn't been afraid, Captain Cecil had told the others that I never turned a hair, I was as cool as a cucumber, he had said, even when that heavy stuff was falling at Dead End. And though they might not pay much attention to all that he said, yet they would have to pay some. I had learnt that I could take it, and sooner or later the others would have to accept me.

Two days later I went up to Potijze again, and this time I stayed there, now in charge of the working party. Jack remained with me for one night, to show me how the work was done and give me the benefit of his experience. 'The men know what to do,' he said, 'they know much better than we do. If there's anything you want to know, ask one of the N.C.O.'s, he'll tell you. Stop work and get the men under cover at once when Jerry starts shelling, and get the wagons and teams away quick when they bring up ammunition. That's about all there is to it. Whatever you do, don't bugger the men about, that's the only unforgivable thing. That, and having unnecessary casualties.'

'Think you'll be all right then?' he asked the next morning

before he went away, using my Christian name for the first time.

'I think so,' I said. I was feeling a little nervous, but very excited.

He stood in the doorway, sucking at his pipe.

'There's half a bottle of whisky left,' he said, 'that ought to last you for a day or two.'

'Oh, I shan't want more than that,' I told him.

Still he did not go away. He blew a cloud of smoke out of his mouth.

'How are you off for cigarettes?' he asked.

I thought I had enough. Anyway, someone had told me there was a canteen a little up the road.

'I shouldn't go outside,' he advised. 'It's always a mistake to go out of a safe place into one that isn't. Look! I've got a packet and I hardly ever smoke them. Take these.'

He insisted on giving me a slightly crumpled packet of Gold Flake out of his pocket.

'Thank you, Jack,' I said. 'I shall be all right.'

'I'll be off then,' he said at last. 'Cheerio! Take care of yourself.'

We had been sleeping since daybreak, now it was the middle of the day, and as soon as Jack had gone I went across the road to see whether the men were getting their dinner. I had twenty men with me, they were on one side of the road, the same side as the position we were preparing, I was on the other. Each of the other batteries in the brigade had a similar working party in the line. A Battery were by themselves, but the officers of B and D were sharing with us the building known as Gibraltar Farm. That was its name on the map, and probably it had been a farm once. Each of us had a little place of his own to sleep in, but we ate most of our meals together in a larger place that was not so strong. We only ate there when it was comparatively quiet outside, for it had no protection on one side. We could look out to the garden, where flowers were still growing, and also some fruit bushes. We had red currants or rhubarb for dinner every day. It was nice to look at the flowers, but we went away at once if shells started to fall.

Work started as soon as it was dark, and went on through the night. We were making pits for the guns, and additional shelters. Every night, ammunition was brought up and had to be unloaded and put away, and then all our work had to be camouflaged and tracks covered before it was light enough for German aeroplanes to see what we had been doing.

I always stayed with the men while work was in progress. They knew what to do, as Jack had said, I didn't have to tell them, I shouldn't have known. I was astonished by their skill. Some of them had been miners, of course they knew how to dig and rivet the sides of shelters, how to place the arches on top and how much weight they could safely take, but even the others were far more proficient than I should have been. I tried to learn from them, watching them as they worked. I listened to their conversation, laughing at their humour, seldom making a remark myself. They talked freely to one another as though I was not there, sometimes I could not understand what they said and often I regretted the differences that separated me from them. I felt shy in their company, shy because I knew nothing about their home lives, only that they were very different from my own. I felt uncomfortable because of my privileged position. But they showed no resentment, and never took advantage of my inexperience. They grumbled a lot, meaning what they said, but saying it to make the others laugh, and because of the quick wit of these townsmen we all did laugh. Sometimes they made remarks about the officers, the Major and Captain Cecil and Josh were their chief butts. Their mimicry was so good that I would almost have believed Josh was there beside us. Because there was no malice in their remarks I laughed as freely as the others, knowing that I should be their next target.

For the first time in my life I, a boy from a Public School, was doing manual work beside men who were manual workers. In a flash of revelation, caused perhaps by the flash of a bursting shell outside, I saw that instead of my being superior to them they were superior to me. But I saw something else, that it did not matter which of us was better, what mattered was that we were working together against a common enemy, the shells that were bumping and banging in the darkness on

41

the other side of our sandbag wall, together we were making the place stronger, so that they should not hurt us.

We were shelled every night. Watching the men I learnt when I ought to feel afraid and when fear was unnecessary. Of a single whizz-bang they would take no notice, but a dozen at the same time could be frightening. Whizz-bangs were the smallest German shells, corresponding to the eighteen-pounders that we ourselves fired. Next in size were the four-twos. They were more disagreeable, but unless one burst within twenty or thirty yards it was unlikely to hurt you, and a good shelter was proof even against a direct hit by a four-two. But only the strongest kept out a five-nine falling even a hundred yards away. Four-twos and five-nines were the commonest shells used against us in forward artillery positions, but there were bigger ones, eight-inch and eleven-inch. These were terrifying, but fortunately we did not often suffer from them, they were used against the heavy guns behind us and the deep dug-outs in Ypres.

I was enjoying myself, but the happiest moment in the twenty four hours was when we stopped work. Then the men went to get their breakfast or supper, whichever they liked to call it, I saw them start it and then went across the road for my own. Day was just breaking. To the west, I could dimly see the ruins of Ypres, and the tall poplars, splintered and mostly dead, but still standing along the canal bank. On the other side, to the east, there was only the grey emptiness of the front line area. There was nothing to be seen there. I could not see the trenches or the infantry in them.

At some time during the night our rations had come up with the ammunition, and with the rations our mail. There were always letters for me, I found them by my plate where my servant had put them when he laid the table for me in my little room. He brought in my breakfast as soon as he saw me coming, and I read my letters while I was eating.

I was as happy as I had ever been. I could not help it. Happy to be where I was and with the night's work safely behind me, and happy because of my home, which letters brought so clearly before me. They took me away from Ypres, I was back in England as I read. My father wrote to me

42

from my own Public School where he had gone to teach for the last part of the summer term, because they were so short of masters. He gave me news of masters I had known, and of boys who had once been my friends only a year ago, but who no longer seemed to have any part in my life. My mother wrote about the Oxford canteen in which she was serving, or about the wounded soldiers who had been up to our house for tea; she was so tired at the end of the day that she hardly knew what to do with herself, she said. My fourteen-year-old sister told me all her cricket scores, and whether they had won their last school match, and about a bicycle ride to Islip. Islip! I could smell the reeds at the side of the river, and see the forget-me-nots and purple loosestrife on the banks.

I could picture them, my father, my mother and my sister. But they could not picture me on the Potijze road, I could not make them understand what it was like. I might tell them I was happy, but that would not make them worry less. German shells could not differentiate between one kind of British soldier and another.

In addition to my letters there was usually a scribbled note for me from one of the others at the wagon lines. How was I? Was there anything I wanted? Josh and the Major had gone into Poperinghe again. The Major had told them to send me another half bottle of whisky. But I hadn't finished the last one yet. I drank the stuff when I was with the others to show them that I liked it, but in fact I did not like it, I had drunk very little since Jack left me.

Then sleep. The noise outside went on, it never stopped, day or night, but I did not hear it. When I woke I went to see how the men were. Then it was time for lunch. And still there was all the long afternoon to look forward to before work started again. Talking to the officers in the other batteries or to strangers who dropped in, reading my book when I had nothing else to do.

We read in the open room, our balcony we called it. Sometimes we took our chairs or substitute empty ammunition boxes outside and sat in the garden, enjoying the afternoon sunshine. Though so much had been destroyed, yet much was left still, some of the willows and poplars still had life in them, and

43

roses were as beautiful and smelled as sweetly here as in an Oxford garden. My servant picked a bunch for me and put them in a jar in my room, and when he saw that I was pleased he found other flowers for me as well. I had almost more than I wanted. Sometimes the concussion of a near shell outside, or my own clumsiness, knocked over one of the jars and water was spilled over my letters or books.

My servant took me to see where a pair of swallows had made their nest on a rafter of one of the shelters. No one disturbed them, everyone used the other entrance. The five young birds had just hatched and we watched the parents feeding them. There seemed as many birds here as there were at home.

I had not expected the war to be like this, and I never found it like this again. At Ypres, even in the summer of 1917, before the great battle began, there was still something of the old world left, something at variance with the war, a sense of homes that had once been lived in and gardens where children had played. At the wagon lines, which were in some fields by a farm, life still went on more or less as usual for the Flemish farmer and his family, and they all smiled when they saw us. In Poperinghe, at one of the souvenir shops, I had bought some pre-war picture postcards of Ypres, one of the Cloth Hall, another of the Cathedral, one of the children in the road by the Menin Gate, and one of sheep grazing in Les Plaines d'Amour outside the town, which was where Captain Cecil had made me walk so fast on the day he took me up to the line. There is no romance in modern war, but youth is romantic and in war, as in love, he looks for beauty and glamour even when it is not there.

I had not yet seen the other side, the fear and demoralisation, the faces of the dead, the horror of the places where men had killed one another, I had not heard the cries of the dying. All that was to come. At Gibraltar Farm I happened to be lucky, we had no casualties during the five or six days that I was there by myself.

Josh was less fortunate when it was his turn to be up there. The shelling was worse, our farm was hit more than once, the balcony was destroyed, one of our men was killed, and an officer in one of the other batteries, and hundreds of rounds of our ammunition, were blown up. Jack said that the loss of the ammunition was our responsibility, his and mine, we ought not to have left it in the houses at the side of the road, we ought to have carried it further away, we should get hauled over the coals, he said. But no one seemed to mind about the ammunition. Everyone was sorry about poor Packer, and poor fat Morrice, the officer in D Battery who had been laughing and joking with me only a few days before. But there was plenty of ammunition in the dump.

And poor Josh was very sorry for himself. He resented my having had such a quiet time. 'It was a blasted picnic all the time you were up there,' he said. I had told him about our red currant pies and how we sat outside in the sunshine. He was angry with me for telling him such a cock-and-bull story, though fortunately I had kept most of my thoughts to myself. They had flattened the place out, he said, I shouldn't be able to recognise it.

During a whole morning I did not once hear his laughter, but in the evening he went into Poperinghe with the Major and Captain Cecil, and he was himself again when they returned. It was his turn to be Orderly Officer on the following day, and I heard him telling Cecil not to lie awake all night so as to see that he got up early. 'Something tells me I'm going to oversleep,' he said, 'and it would be a pity for you to lose your beauty sleep.'

6

In Action at Last

Now that my loneliness had passed away I could see I had
been lucky in being brought so gradually into the war. If
everything had happened at once, if I had gone straight into
action in the middle of a battle, my ignorance and the mistakes
I should have made might have damaged my relationship with
the others far more seriously; and the shock of battle and
sudden death, before I was prepared for them, would probably
have prevented my finding the calm happiness I was now
enjoying. Now I could fairly claim to have been under fire,
not just once for a minute or two, but day after day for a
week on end. I had been in charge of a working party in the
line, I had learnt the names of all the men in the battery
(and a few of the horses), and the other officers were
beginning to accept me. Jack was friendly, and Frank had
dropped his tone of sarcasm when he spoke to me, the Major
looked at me with amused tolerance, and Captain Cecil
defended me against Josh's mocking remarks.

Now I only had to wait for the beginning of the great attack,
then my experience would be complete, I thought. But the
attack was a long time coming. No more work was done at
the position on the Potijze Road and the working party was
brought back to the wagon lines. We were transferred to a
different division, from the Scottish Thistle Division to the
Lancashire Red Rose one, I was sent up to hand over the place
we had made to another battery, we were to go instead to a
position a few hundred yards in front of the canal.

But still we waited.

'What are we waiting for? Isn't there going to be a battle?'
Jack said hopefully.

'They're waiting for the weather to break,' the Major told him. 'They don't want to make things too easy for us. Everything went like clockwork last time and they're afraid that if it happens again we may lose our initiative. But if the ground gets churned up a bit first then we shall be properly tested.'

I did not mind waiting now, we were all content to be at the wagon lines. There were expeditions into Poperinghe and rides in the afternoon. I fell off my horse twice in one day. Captain Cecil said he would have to give me instruction, I could see for myself, he said, the importance of having a good seat. Falling off my horse was not the only danger, German long-range guns were active, hardly a night passed without shells coming over and some fell in our camp, we had casualties to men as well as horses.

What were we waiting for?

July was more than half over before we went into action at a place called "The Summer House", in front of the canal. Only three officers went up to the gun line at first. The Major took Edward with him, and I, to my great satisfaction, was the third.

So I was with the battery in action at last. Most of our firing was done by night. We were given an area to shoot at, but we chose our own targets, tracks leading up to the line, trench intersections, places where movement had been observed or from which machine-gun fire had been reported. We fired about two hundred and fifty rounds every night. I watched Edward working out the shoots. He calculated angles and ranges on our large-scale map-board, and then gave the orders and times of firing to the Number Ones of each gun. It looked straight-forward, I was sure I could do it, and on the third night I asked the Major to let me. He was amused by my enthusiasm and agreed at once, but he told Edward to check my figures. 'Chuck the things where you like,' he said. 'You're just as likely to hit Fritzes in one place as in another. But don't take any risks with the range, you must never shoot short, that's the only thing for which there's no forgiveness.'

But he told me in the morning that I had disturbed his rest. 'You were running in and out of the place all night long,'

47

he said, 'no one could get any sleep. Fire all the stuff at one go and be done with it.'

'But it's called harassing fire,' I said.

'You've got it wrong,' he said, 'It's the Fritzes who are to be harassed, not us. Get it over by a Christian hour, nothing after two o'clock.'

'But if the Germans get to know that we don't fire after two o'clock,' I protested, 'they'll do all their work then.'

'Well, good luck to them!' he said. 'That's what brains are for.'

I was disappointed, I wanted to go on all through the night. Four rounds rapid fire from each gun ten times a night, that was the way to inflict the greatest number of casualties on the enemy, and in the end grudgingly he allowed me one or two bursts of firing during dinner. The concussion brought down bits of the walls and ceiling of our dug-out. I had quite spoilt his soup one night, he said.

We ourselves were under fire for a considerable part of the day and night, but we had good dug-outs and we seemed luckier than the other batteries. It was the beginning of the good fortune which we enjoyed all through the battle. D Battery had a direct hit on their officers' mess, one officer was killed, one wounded, and the third badly shell-shocked. A Battery position was so heavily shelled that more than once it had to be abandoned, and their officers came to spend the rest of the day with us, much to the Major's satisfaction.

He loved company, he must have someone to talk to, his own subalterns were no use to him, he said. Frank was always writing a letter to his girl, he complained; I was always reading; Jack would sit and listen to him, but he always agreed with everything he said and that was dull; Edward disagreed with everything and that was worse. Josh was the only one of us who had anything to say for himself, and then only at the wagon lines; at the guns he was always listening for the sound of the next shell and could pay no attention to anything that was said to him.

We had a lot of visitors in our mess. Every officer in the brigade knew there would be a drink for him if he cared to go over to C Battery and sit and talk with the Major, and passing strangers were often invited in. When there was no one in the mess for him to talk to he went outside and talked to the men, with whom he was very popular. He had the gift of being able to talk with everyone, but he did not want to do all the talking, they must talk back to him. Edward also had the gift of being able to talk easily to the men, he was not shy with them, as I was, he seemed to know something about the home life of every one of them.

I was enjoying myself. After the long uncertainty it was very satisfying to find that I was not unduly afraid of shell-fire and that I could carry out the tasks that were given me. As yet I had been given nothing difficult to do, but I hardly realised this. Each day was an end in itself, one thought about to-morrow, but not about the day after. It seemed after a few days that I had always been with the battery in action and that it would go on like this for ever. I liked and admired both Edward and the Major, I did not talk much to either of them, I listened to their talking, either to each other or to one of our visitors. When there was nothing else to do, I read. There was a ledge on the top of our dug-out where I could lie and read in the sunshine, able to dive inside within a second or two if I heard a shell coming close.

In the evening from the same place I used to watch the aeroplane fights through my field glasses. Often they were flying at such a height that I could not see the markings on the machines, the red blue and white rings of one of ours, or the black Maltese Cross of an enemy, and when one fell I could not always tell who had been victorious. Sometimes the plane fell like a stone, but more often it turned over and over, fluttering to the ground like a leaf in autumn. I was still unfamiliar with death, and was distressed to think of the man inside, even if he was a German. There was no baling out from aeroplanes in those days.

'Is there any chance of the man being alive still?' I once asked the Major when together we had been watching one flutter down.

'Not a cat in hell's chance,' he replied, and went on whistling.

49

I paid my first visit to an Observation Post. Edward was going up to register the guns and he took me with him. He was a little more friendly now, but was still rather inaccessible, his attitude of aloofness to me was almost the only thing I could have wished to be different.

The O.P. was in one of our support trenches, only a few hundred yards behind the front line, I had not been so close to the line before. Each gun at the battery fired in turn, and after the bursting shell had been observed Edward spoke over the telephone, changing its range or angle and fired it again until it was accurately on the target. I stood beside him in the trench, watching the shell bursts. He told me to keep my head down, and I tilted my helmet over my forehead, as he had done, so that only my eyes were exposed over the top of the trench. There was not much to see. Only trenches in the foreground, I could not tell where ours ended and the enemy's began. Nothing was to be seen in any of them, just a succession of trenches. But in the distance, about a mile away, country began again, and colour. I could see grass and trees on the top of a low ridge, red-brick houses and the tower of a church looking almost undamaged. It was a pleasure as well as a surprise to see these ordinary things: the low green hill, the houses, a church. They contrasted so happily with the trench scars immediately in front of us. The village was Passchendaele, Edward told me, but the name meant nothing to either of us. It was just one of the villages on their side of the line. Zonnebeke and St Julien, Langemarck and Polekappelle were others whose names I had noticed on our map board.

Edward addressed an occasional remark to me about the shooting. So many guns were firing that it was not easy to pick out our own shells, and if I took my eyes off the target, a grey block of concrete nearly a mile away, one of many, I was afraid of losing it. German guns were firing back at our side of the line and two or three times we had to duck our heads when a shell fell close to us. He was satisfied at last with the guns' shooting and told the signallers to pack up their equipment. Then we walked back the way we had come, along trenches at first, over the open when we came nearer to the battery.

A day or two later we received our orders for the great attack, though neither the time nor the day was yet given to us. We were to move forward from the Summer House two hours after Zero, the time of the launching of the attack, and go into action again in a position not far behind our present front line. But we were only to stay there for a few hours. We were to go forward again, over no-man's-land, nearly to St. Julien, at present more than a mile inside the German line. The orders were worked out in great detail: all our targets for the first part of the attack, the exact moment when we were to cease fire, and when we were to start again from the second position. And we were to send out a forward observing officer who would go up with the infantry and send back information about the progress of the attack. Jack was detailed to go.

But before the attack started there were changes in the battery. Major John, the commander of B Battery was wounded for the second or third time and Captain Cecil was promoted to the command in his place. Edward was given the captaincy in our battery and went down to the wagon lines, which was the place for the captain and second-in-command. We were none of us sorry that Cecil was leaving us. I ought to have been, for he had been friendly to me from the beginning, but I had less need of his friendship now and therefore accepted what the others said about him, and we were all pleased to have Edward for our captain.

I went down to the wagon lines for a few nights before the battle started, but I returned on the last afternoon, the afternoon of Y-Day, as it was called. Jack and I went up together. Poor Jack was in very low spirits. 'I wonder what's the chance of my being alive at this time tomorrow,' he said. I told him not to take any unnecessary risks. 'I shan't,' he replied. 'I'm not that sort of person, you can set your mind at rest about that.'

But we did take an unnecessary risk that very afternoon. Jack was going to see Colonel Richardson for his final instructions. The Colonel's headquarters were in a deep dug-out in the ramparts of Ypres and we walked through the middle of the town instead of going round on the outside, which would have been a little further. It seemed quiet when we came to the outskirts, and I was pleased at the thought of walking through the famous town. But almost at once we heard the familiar sound of big shells coming over and started to run. I did not know the way, I followed Jack. We crouched behind a great mound of rubble and stones, a shell burst on the other side of it not far away, I covered the back of my neck with both my hands. Then we ran again. We ran under a high archway, over more piles of stones, bending down whenever we heard a shell coming. Jack told me afterwards that we had run through the Cathedral. Then we were running down the middle of a road, the sound of the shells was behind us now, but we did not stop running. We came out into an open space, with water in front of us. This was the moat of the old city, there was a line of deep dug-outs by the water, and one of these was the Colonel's headquarters.

We went down a lot of steps. It was very dark inside, the walls were dripping with water, there was no air, it was a relief to be safe from the shells, but I was glad we did not have to live in a place like this; I thought the Summer House was much preferable. We were given a friendly welcome by Colonel Richardson and Captain Cherry, his smiling adjutant.

'What's it like outside?' Cherry asked us.

Jack told him that we'd had to run, we were still panting.

'Well, if it's any comfort to you,' Cherry said, 'for every shell we get, the Boche has been getting four or five.'

The Colonel began talking to Jack. It would all be perfectly straightforward, he said. The Boche had been given such a hammering that he would not know whether it was last night or to-morrow morning, when the attack started. It would be just like the last show over again. Jack would simply have to follow the infantry, unrolling telephone wire as he went, and stopping every now and then to let them know at headquarters how far the advance had gone.

'Just like going for a country walk,' Cherry said.

Jack was nodding his head at everything they said to him, but I knew him well enough to be sure that he was thinking

52

it would not be at all like a country walk. The Colonel told him there was no need for him to go putting his head into danger, his job was to send back information, and all the information in the world would be no use unless he was alive to send it.

'A living dog is better than a dead lion,' Cherry said. He added that if the show was a success, and everything pointed in that direction, then it might mean the end of the war and that we should all be home before Christmas.

They were very encouraging and I was greatly cheered by what they said about our prospects of success, but Jack said, after we had left them and were walking along the canal bank on our way to the battery, that he had not been impressed. 'I could be optimistic,' he said, 'if I lived at the bottom of a place like that. Bloody optimistic,' he added.

The Major also thought Jack was in need of encouragement when we arrived, and he gave him some and poured out some for himself. Then they took their mugs to one of the beds at the back of the dug-out while Frank sat in the doorway, where the light was better, working out our barrage fire for the next morning. 'Don't speak to him,' the Major had warned us, 'he's always like a bear with a sore head when he gets on to this job.' I thought he was hoping to provoke him, but Frank took no notice, he went quietly on, saying figures to himself, writing them down, working with entire concentration. Jack had told me he was the only person in the battery who knew how to work out the barrage for an attack, it was impossible for an ordinary person to understand, he said. I sat down beside him without speaking, I wanted to learn how to work out a barrage and I knew that he would let me ask him questions when he had finished.

I had a worry of my own to think about, for I was to lead the guns forward to the second position at Z+120, that is to say two hours after the battle started. I had been up to this position twice. It was terrible, nothing but shell-holes. And a ditch called the Bellewaardebeke in the middle of them. I could not imagine how guns would be able to move at all over such ground, and at present it was within sight of the enemy lines. I had gone for the first time with Colonel Richardson

53

and an officer from each battery, we had just looked at the place, made unfavourable comments about it, and come away. We had gone very early in the morning, it was misty and therefore comparatively safe, we were not under enemy observation. But when I went for the second time, with the Major, to show him the place and to reconnoitre the way there for our guns, the sun came out while we were standing on the position and we saw the German line staring down at us, not more than half a mile away and looking much nearer, a low bare hostile ridge curving round us. But we hardly stopped to look at it, we came away quickly without staying to think about the best way of getting the guns up.

This was the reason for my worrying now. The orders stated explicitly that field batteries were to keep off the roads. They were to be left for heavier transport. I was to take our guns along a track that went through the grounds of a château, past some ornamental waters fed by the same stream, the Bellewaardebeke, and then to follow along the stream until we came to our position. But the track in the château grounds had been heavily shelled and the water had escaped into the shell-holes, the place was not much better than a swamp. I was afraid the guns would be stuck if I took them past the château.

'You go by the road,' the Major said. 'Go whichever way you think is best, don't take any notice of the orders.'

I couldn't decide. If I went by the road I might find our way blocked by other transport, and it was just possible that I might meet a staff officer acting as a military policeman, who would order me to turn round and go back, and that would certainly make us late. But if I went the château way I might find the ground too soft for our horses, I might not get up to the position at all.

I wondered if I ought to go and have another look at the track, and see how many new shell holes had appeared since I had last been there and how much water was in them. But the thought of going up there again daunted me. Even the Major had disliked the place and had said you wouldn't catch him going there for a swim before breakfast. And Jack had told me that he made it a rule never to go anywhere unless he was

54

ordered to. 'You'll have plenty of chances of getting killed,' he had said, 'without going out of your way to look for others.' If visibility had been poor I might have gone, but the evening was clear, I did not go. I couldn't help worrying about it, and wondering which way I ought to go. 'The important thing is to get off quick,' Frank said, when I had a chance of consulting him, 'before the place is blocked by everyone else.'

I went outside with him when he had the orders ready to give to the Number Ones of each gun. He explained them to each one, making sure that they understood them and that they had everything in readiness for the morning. Then we went back into the dug-out. Time passed very slowly. Jack had already gone. 'The longer I stay here, the harder I shall find it to go away,' he had said. Frank was continually getting up to look at the orders again or to verify something on the map. I was still wondering which way to go. Sometimes I decided in favour of the track. But then I thought of the soft black earth and the deep holes in the middle of the way, and all the water in them. It seemed madness to think of going off the road, and I changed my mind again. The Major was in a bad temper, he snapped at everything we said and was continually finding fault with the servants. We hardly spoke during dinner. But their obvious anxiety was a help to me. If they had been quite unperturbed I should have been more than ever distrustful of my own powers. But they were both worrying, so it was right that I should worry also, and I made up my mind that I would leave the decision about the way until I had actually started. I would be guided by my feeling when the moment for decision came.

Time dragged by. I couldn't go to my bed of wire netting because the Major was sitting on it, and Frank was still working. At about midnight there was a sudden fierce burst of shellfire outside. The concussion blew out all our candles. We were left in darkness, I heard cries of pain, about a dozen men came falling into our little dug-out, it was so full that no one could move, and no one could find matches to relight the candles. 'He's hit,' someone was saying. 'Who's hit?' shouted the Major angrily. 'For God's sake, get outside and stay out, and bring in whoever it is.'

It was Sergeant Appleby, the senior N.C.O., in the gun-line, our youngest sergeant, and one of the best-liked men in the battery. Our guns had just finished firing, the men were returning to their dug-outs when they were caught by the German shells, and they had rushed into the nearest shelter, but Sergeant Appleby had been hit by a fragment of shell. I thought he was dying, I was not accustomed to seeing so much blood and pain, but in fact he was not very badly wounded. They took him away to the dressing station on a stretcher, and he was back with us before the end of the summer.

Then at last it was quiet and I could go to sleep. But the Major was still talking in an angry voice to someone who had come in. 'Just a lot of bloody wind,' I heard him saying. 'Anyone would think this was the first battle there had ever been.' But I passed away into unconsciousness, of the battle and everything else.

7

Zero Hour and Z-Day

Zero Hour was 3.50. Frank had told one of the signallers
to call us at a quarter past three. We got up at once, and after
putting on the few clothes we had taken off we went outside,
leaving the Major still asleep. It was very quiet, hardly a gun
was firing, as though all the world knew what was going to
happen and was waiting in silent expectancy.

'Do you think the Germans know?' I asked Frank.

'Oh yes,' he said, 'we always tell them. They may not know
whether it's today or tomorrow, but all the firing we've done
in the last week can mean only one thing.'

The morning was cold, there was a feeling of wetness in the
air, but whether it was just the mist before dawn or a sign
that rain was coming I could not tell. All the men were up;
I could see them moving about behind the guns. Some of them
were carrying shells from the pit where ammunition was kept
and putting them down beside the guns in readiness. I heard
the clink of the brass cases, one against another, as the shells
were put down. We went to speak to the Number Ones. Frank
had the big battery watch in his hand and he gave the correct
time to each of them. We were going to fire a creeping barrage,
that is to say we had to increase the range of our guns by a
hundred yards every four minutes, so that our attacking
infantry could follow closely behind the curtain of fire, and
each N.C.O. was responsible for firing the correct number of
rounds in every minute and adding to the range at the right
time. There was very little talking. Everyone was alert, each
man had his work to do and he was doing it; he did not want
to be distracted.

Then we took up our position in the centre of the battery and about fifteen yards behind the guns. My eyes had grown accustomed to the darkness by this time. I could see the line of poplars on the canal bank behind us; by daylight you could see they were all dead, there was not a green leaf among them, but some were still standing at their full height or nearly, others had been split in half, a few had completely gone, there was just a gap in the line to show where one had been. And on the other side in the east, over the German trenches, the sky already looked lighter.

'Five minutes to go,' Frank shouted, looking at the big watch, and each of the Number Ones raised an arm in acknowledgment to show that he had heard. He told me that he had ordered his breakfast for half past four, and when he had finished he would come outside and take over from me so that I could have mine. 'And by the time you've finished the limbers ought to be up here,' he said.

It was still very quiet, the quietness gave a sense of unreality to the morning. How could so great an occasion be unheralded! But I could feel the palpitation of my heart.

One gun behind us on the other side of the canal fired a second too soon. Then Frank blew a loud blast on his whistle, but I only heard the first note, the bombardment began as he was blowing, all the guns in the Ypres Salient opened fire and the roar of artillery drowned every other sound. All the guns in the Salient! It sounded like all the guns in the world. It sounded as though the sky was falling, as though the thunder of the guns had cracked it, as though the world itself was breaking into pieces. Our shells were breaking it. Low down, all along the eastern horizon, I saw their red flashes as they burst, spurts of fire in the darkness. And now the German rockets were going up, their S.O.S. signals, the call for artillery support: red, green and yellow lights, and showers of beautiful golden rain. Frank shouted something at me, waving his arm in the direction of the rockets, but I could not hear what he was saying. A few German shells came back at us, one here, one there, a big one a little way in front of us, a salvo on the canal bank, but for the most part they were falling a long way in front, on the infantry, on the trenches from which the attack was now being made. We should get it later probably, I thought; but we had no casualties at this time.

Daylight came. I had been wondering what I should see. I was expecting it to look altogether different, but it was the same, the same as any other day—the same flat landscape, the broken trees and shattered farms. Some lines of infantry were slowly moving forward, one man behind the other, a long line, going up towards the front. That was the only difference.

After half an hour our rate of fire dropped from four to three rounds a minute for each gun, then to two. Frank went to get his breakfast, I was left alone, I wondered whether I should know what to do if anything unexpected happened. But nothing happened, everything was working automatically, our guns firing, German shells throwing up fountains of earth on the left and on the right, but not in the middle of us.

Then it was my turn to go inside. The Major was just getting up; he was sitting on his bed, yawning. 'Anything happening outside?' he asked, but I could tell that his nonchalance was put on, for when his servant brought in his plate of eggs and bacon he swore at him for clumsiness and did not answer when I spoke to him. I hurried through my breakfast, I wanted to go outside again, and I had decided what to do about the guns. I would start off along the track, I would use the track for more than half the way, but when I came to the road that curved round the grounds of the château, if it was not blocked. I would turn right instead of going straight across into the gardens. This would bring me to the main Potijze Road in a few hundred yards, and then I had to turn left along the main road and I should come to the Bellewaardebeke in less than half a mile, and once there no one would know that I had not come through the château gardens.

I went outside again. Almost at the same moment the limbers arrived. Josh was leading them, they drove up behind the guns at a gallop. Josh's face was very stern, like myself he had evidently been expecting that everything would be different on the morning of the Great Battle and he had not yet realised that it was like any other day. Josh was not a light weight, and now with all his equipment on his back, haversack and water bottle, cape rolled up, field glasses, gas mask at

59

the alert position, steel helmet very straight on his head, he certainly looked prepared for war.

'What's this?' Frank shouted out to him. 'The Charge of the Heavy Brigade? or the Iron Duke at Waterloo?'

Josh did not smile. This was no time for smiling; and besides, though he could make jokes against himself he was not pleased when other people made them. He got off his horse and came over to us. 'What's happening?' he said. 'Who's winning?' But there was no news yet.

Now it was time for me to start. The battery had ceased firing, the guns had been limbered up, they were ready for me. I was going with them by myself, the others were to follow later with the wagons which Edward had brought up, and all the rest of the ammunition. The servants were busy packing up our things. I gave an order to the first team behind me and began to walk, I could hear the guns following me. It was as though some other person had pressed a button to set us all in motion, the machine was working automatically. Now I had come to the beginning of the track, I was walking along it, all our six-horse gun teams were stepping along behind me. I was conscious of a feeling of anxiety. This was the first time the Major had given me a job to do on my own, I was determined not to fail him. In fact there was no difficulty. We were hardly delayed at all, we had made a good start, no other batteries were on the track yet, we did not fall into any of the holes, we were not shelled. When we came to the road, I looked along it, saw that it was clear, and turned to the right. The die was cast. Some infantry transport was moving along the road; I got in behind it, nobody blocked our way, we blocked nobody else's. I saw a tank on the road, two others were stuck in the mud at a little distance from it, or perhaps they had been hit. I saw some German prisoners, no one was guarding them, they were coming back by themselves. I saw some of our wounded walking back. In little more than an hour, soon after seven o'clock, the guns were behind the Bellewaardebeke, ready to open fire again for the second phase of the attack.

Out of curiosity, while waiting for the others, I went to look inside the château gardens. There were a lot of new holes, the ground looked very soft, there was more confusion than I had found on the road; a gun, not one of ours, one belonging to another brigade, had fallen into a shell-hole, the gunners had fixed lanyards to the wheels and were all pulling on them, while the horses strained to extricate it. I was thankful we had gone by the road.

The rest of the battery arrived, and the other batteries of the brigade. We were next to the road, on the right hand side of it, B Battery was on our right, A and D were on the other side of the road in the grounds of the château. We asked one another for news. Someone said we had captured our first objectives, but nothing was certain yet. It was no good asking the walking wounded, they always said the attack was going well, they were so pleased to be out of it.

'I saw a lot of prisoners as we were coming up,' Josh said.

'Not many,' Frank said. 'Nothing like so many as last time.'

Cherry rang up to ask if we were in position. Everything was going well so far, he said, we had gained all our first objectives.

The time had now come to launch the second attack. All the guns opened fire again, the noise was even louder than before, for the other batteries were closer to us than they had been, there were field guns in a long line for as far as I could see. Edward went back to his advanced wagon lines, taking the teams and all the limbers and wagons with him. They would be wanted again for our second advance, but they could not stay up here; we were too close to the enemy. It was too early yet to feel sure that he had been defeated.

The Major and Frank went up to reconnoitre the way for our second advance. They went with Colonel Richardson and the other battery commanders. Josh and I were left alone. In front of us, across the Bellewaardebeke, the ground rose gently for five or six hundred yards to a low ridge. That ridge had been our front line in the morning. We could not see over it in front of us, but we could see other ridges on the right. All those had been German-held in the morning. Whose were they now? We did not know.

Cherry rang up again. He did not sound so optimistic this time. Some enemy strong points were still holding out, our advance had been held up for the moment, we were to reduce range, we were to repeat the last part of our firing programme, in support of another attack which was just going in.

'Look at the road!' Josh said to me.

It was packed with guns and wagons and other transport. All the way up to the top of the ridge in front of us, and for some way behind. But it was not moving, nothing was going over the crest. What was wrong? 'I can put two and two together as well as anyone else,' Josh said. 'They're not going on because they can't, because the Boche is still there and would see them if they went over the crest.'

I waited. Surely the line would start moving soon. Cherry had said it was only in one or two places that we had been held up. Surely the next attack would be successful. But the long line on the road did not move.

'I don't know about you, young fellow,' Josh said after a time, 'but I could do with a drop of Scotch and a bite of something.' I said that everything was packed up and the Major had said that nothing was to be unpacked on this position.

'Oh, that's all my eye,' Josh said. 'I can tell you I don't exactly enjoy fighting a battle at the best of times, but if the Major or anyone else thinks I'm going to fight one on an empty stomach—well, he can think again, that's all.'

I could not think of this as a battle, it was altogether different from any pictures of battles I had seen, it was like an ordinary day. And yet it was different. For one thing there was that long line of stationary wagons and guns on the road. Why didn't the Boche start shelling it? It would be terrible if he did, they were so close together they could hardly turn round. And in myself I felt a difference, a sense of expectancy that I had never felt on an ordinary day. Something was going to happen, but I had no idea what it would be. When the Major returned we should go forward again, over no-man's-land, into the very middle of the battlefield. That, at any rate, was what we had been told. Josh said it didn't look like another move, not yet anyway. But if the German guns were still in their original positions, why weren't they shelling us? The situation was obscure, Cherry said. We were to go on firing at a slower rate, and at a range not much greater than we had started at.

Josh had gone away, now he called me over to join him. He had poured out two mugs of whisky and he was sitting on the top of a shallow trench with his legs dangling inside and a plate of thick bully beef sandwiches beside him. The whisky was a good deal stronger than anything I was accustomed to pour out for myself.

'What did Medley say?' I asked. Medley was our cook, I had heard the Major telling him that on no account was anything to be unpacked except on his orders.

'He didn't say anything,' Josh answered shortly. 'Medley and I have a very good understanding together if you really want to know.'

He startled me by suddenly bawling out something in German, and he got up and went quickly over to the road. I saw that some German prisoners had stopped and were helping themselves to a drink out of our water cart. I followed him, he was talking at a great rate, I had not realised that he could speak German so well.

'Just like their blasted impudence,' he said, when he had driven them away.

I was rather sorry for them, they looked very wretched, 'I expect they felt they could do with a drop of something,' I said.

'Don't talk so damned soft,' he said. 'That cart may have to last us for a couple of days. Anyway, why should we give them anything? They're responsible for all this. If it wasn't for them we should be at home, I should be sitting down to steak and onions instead of eating bully beef and sweating my guts out in this god-forsaken country.'

He put a guard on the water cart and told him that no one was to drink out of it except men in our own battery. Hewlett was the man he told to guard it. Hewlett was one of our battery rogues. He had been the Major's servant once until he was sacked for some act of dishonesty, which he denied, but he and the Major had continued to be on very good terms, and within a few days the Major had recommended him for the Military Medal, for putting out a dump of burning ammunition which was likely to blow up at any moment. But even I should have known better than to choose Hewlett for a guard if I wanted to be obeyed. During the course of the day I saw him pouring out water for two other prisoners. He was speaking to them in his Yorkshire dialect, they were replying in German, but they seemed to understand one another very well.

It was not until midday that the transport on the road began to move. Then all the guns and wagons turned round and came back. So the battle had not gone according to plan. Cherry admitted that we had not gained all our objectives, and that it seemed unlikely now we should have to move before the next day. When the guns had all gone back the enemy began shelling the road, it was deserted by this time, but we suffered some casualties, our first during the day.

Some time later Frank and the Major returned. They were nearly exhausted and very discouraged. Frank said he had never known a worse day, they had been chased by shells wherever they went, not to mention aeroplanes and machine-gun fire, he didn't know how they were still alive. 'Talk about casualties,' he said. 'There were dead men all over the place, ours and theirs, sometimes two or three on top of one another, you had to look where you were going so as not to tread on them.' Some of them had been there for weeks, he said, but most of them had been killed that morning. 'And the wounded,' he said. 'Crying for help, and no one taking the least notice of them.'

'Why not?' Josh said.

'Everyone too exhausted. And besides, it wasn't possible to walk about in all that shellfire. And the doctors already had their hands full.'

I sat in silence, listening to all that he said. I had not seen the dead yet, not like this, I dreaded seeing them. Even Josh was silent. He had poured out a drink for both of them, and one for himself too. I did not want another one, I was too dejected. In spite of all appearances to the contrary I had been expecting them to bring back good news.

'It's utter lunacy,' the Major was saying. 'We shell the place for a month till there isn't a yard of ground left that isn't a shell-hole, and then they expect the infantry to be able to advance and they tell us to move our guns up there.'

There was no road, he said, there was nothing at all, it would have been utterly impossible to take guns up there even if the German positions had been captured. 'Why don't they go and look at the place and see it for themselves?' he said.

We had our tea. Edward had come up from the wagon lines to find out the latest news and when the limbers would be wanted for the advance. 'There won't be any advance,' the Major said. 'I'm telling you, it was as much as a man could do to walk about there. Guns! Why, you couldn't push a bicycle up there, or a ruddy pram.' Frank told him about the dead men and about the aeroplanes that had shot at them.

'Looks as though we can call it a day then,' Edward said.

'You can call it whatever you bloody well like,' said the Major, 'but there's not going to be another advance.' He had been drinking ever since they came back.

Edward went away again and the rain began. At first it was only a drizzle, but it turned into a heavy rain as daylight faded. Now it was our rockets that went up from the infantry in front of us, two or three times during the evening we had to fire on our S.O.S. lines, which were constantly being changed as fresh orders came in from Brigade Headquarters. No one seemed to know where our front line was, or the enemy's, or whether he was making an attack.

'Of course he isn't,' the Major said, 'he's got more sense. It's just a lot of wind, no one in his senses is going to make an attack on a night like this.'

I hoped he was right. If the Germans recaptured the ground they had lost in the morning we should find ourselves almost in the front line. Gradually the firing on both sides died down, now we had only the rain to contend with. The Major was playing hell with the servants, calling them a lot of lazy bastards, threatening to return them all to duty.

'Go easy, Major,' Josh said. 'They haven't done so badly, it's not exactly been an easy day for them either.'

'How the hell do you know whether a day's been easy or

65

not? I suppose they've been making meals for you all day and that's why you think it's been difficult for them.'

Frank advised us to keep out of his way. 'He's always like this after a battle,' he said. 'I know how to deal with him.' I was anxious about Jack, we had heard nothing from him since early in the day, but Frank told me not to worry, Jack knew how to look after himself, he said, he had probably found a better place for himself for the night than we had.

Our place was certainly nothing to boast about, it was very different from the safety and comfort of the Summer House. There was a shallow trench, barely three feet deep, and on one side of it two small excavations had been dug, a little below the level of the trench. Frank and the Major were in the larger hole, Josh and I in the other, there was just room for our two valises side by side on the ground. I told Josh I was sorry that the Major had been so beastly to him when he was sticking up for the servants, but he only laughed and said he did not mind what anyone said to him. Hard words didn't cut your flesh, he said; what was much more serious was the thinness of earth on our shelter. 'It may keep out the rain,' he said, 'but I'm damned sure it won't keep out anything else.'

Even the rain was not kept out. I woke up early, soon after it was light, and saw that water was trickling down into our hole from the trench outside. It was still raining. I woke up Josh, who was between myself and the wall. If we stayed where we were the water would soon be over our clothes, I said. He went to wake up the servants and told them to make tea for us all and then to get on with breakfast. Frank and the Major we found, were in a much worse plight than ourselves, they had not woken up in time, the water in their hole was deeper than ours, all their clothes were soaked. I thought the Major's temper would be worse than ever and tried to keep out of his way, but he had completely recovered.

'You were all pretty glum last night,' he said while we were eating our breakfast. 'Couldn't get a cheep out of any of you. What was the matter?'

'It must have been the rain,' Josh said, 'and if it goes on much longer we shall all need lifebelts.'

The Major went away to see how the men were. 'Who's

66

winning the war this morning?' I heard him calling out. It was his usual morning greeting to them and I heard a great answering shout from every man on the position—'They are!' 'Not so loud,' the Major told them, laughing, 'the fellows on the Staff will hear you. They think we are!' He was in very high spirits when he came back to us. 'You can just see the muzzles of the guns sticking out of the water,' he said. 'So that's all right, we can still fire them. But I wonder if they've got any boats. We could take the guns up by boat if they still want us to advance.' He said he could hardly wait for *The Times* to come, he was so eager to read about our victory.

Jack turned up during the morning, tired and dirty, but otherwise all right. I thought he was more cheerful than usual. 'Of course it was a bloody awful failure,' he said, 'but I'd been expecting that, so I wasn't particularly depressed.' He went down to the wagon lines, and in the afternoon Edward came up with the rations and full wagons of ammunition, and when he saw how wet Frank and the Major were he suggested that they also should go down and that he should stay up in their place. The Major thought this was a very good idea. He had already rendered us one great service, he had found an empty dug-out about a hundred yards behind the water-logged trenches where we had spent the previous night. I had heard Frank say that the Major could smell a good dug-out if there was one within a mile of us, and certainly he had found a very good one. 'Of course it was the first thing I saw yesterday,' he said, 'but there were other people in it then. But it's always worth keeping your eye on a good place and when I saw the other fellows going away I was into it before you could say "knife".' It was strong and clean and comfortable, and so large that there was room in it not only for ourselves and our servants but for all the signallers as well. It was marked on the map as "Lancer Farm" and was our home for the next five or six weeks.

It was not a dug-out in the ordinary sense of the word, in Flanders you could not dig down to a depth of more than one or two feet because you came to water. But you could strengthen houses or farm buildings of any kind by reinforcing walls and the roof with rubble-filled sandbags or blocks of concrete. The Germans were better at this than we were, probably because they could employ forced Belgian labour. and every building behind their line was converted into a small fort, with slits through which machine-guns could be fired. These were the pill-boxes, as they came to be called later. Almost indestructible by shellfire, they were extremely difficult to capture, and time after time during the fighting of 1917 our attacking infantry overran a line of pill-boxes and advanced to the top of the ridge behind them, only to be shot at from behind and forced to retire by unwounded enemy soldiers, unaffected by our barrage fire, who had come out of the forts. There were fewer of these forts behind our line, we had to wait until we captured the German ones. Then they afforded us invaluable protection in spite of facing the wrong way.

But the place the Major had found for us was British-made. Before going away he told Edward that he would take as many men as possible with him. 'I'll leave you enough to fire the guns,' he said, 'but no more. You've seen for yourself what happened to Frank and me last night and we were lucky not to be shelled as well. There's nothing by the guns fit for a Christian even for one night, nothing that would keep out an orange, and if he starts chucking five-nines about there'll be hell to pay. We can't do anything about it until the weather improves, but that's why I don't intend to leave more men up here than I have to.'

Then he and Frank went off to the wagon lines, Josh and I took our valises into Lancer Farm, and Edward stayed with us, in command of the battery for the time being.

In the late afternoon, when enemy shelling had died down, I went outside to do what I had felt no inclination for while shellfire on the position was so intense. I found a shell-hole on the other side of the Bellewaardebeke dry enough to squat down in and lowered my breeches, listening anxiously for the sound of a shell coming behind me. But I had chosen a lucky moment, I did what I had come out to do, pulled up my breeches, and returned to the security of our home as quickly as possible. By the next day there was a latrine, and even a strip of sacking at my back made me feel less vulnerable to the enemy.

Some of my experiences at the front proved easier than expected, but I had not anticipated how disagreeable others would be.

A few day later the Major returned with either Jack or Frank, and then it was our turn to go down and find dry clothes and enjoy an evening in Poperinghe. Now I felt a real soldier, I had taken part in a battle, I was as excited as a schoolboy going home for the holidays. A friendly Heavy Gunner with a car saw us walking and stopped to pick us up. We drove past the Menin Gate, through Ypres and all the way to Vlamertinghe, where the wagon lines were.

8

Inside Lancer Farm

The rain went on for two or three days, effectively putting an end to any possibility of further infantry action for the present. The Major wanted another spell at the wagon lines, and Edward, Josh and I went up to Lancer Farm again.

The infantry could not attack, but the artillery firing never stopped, day and night on both sides it continued. We were getting through our ammunition at a great rate and in constant need of fresh supplies. Often the wagons came up twice in one day.

I was out by the guns one morning at a time when half a dozen wagons on the road were being unloaded. The road passed between our guns and the grounds of the château, going on to Zonnebeke and into the German lines. Shells began to fall on or near the road and one horse was wounded. To be shelled at a time when wagons and teams were up was almost the worst thing that could befall a battery; horses became frightened and drivers could not dismount, they had to stay where they were, in a very vulnerable position. All one could do was to get the wagons unloaded as quickly as possible and then send them away.

Sergeant Denmark, the senior N.C.O. on the position, was directing the unloading, showing the gunners where to put the shells as they brought them across from the road. The task was nearly finished, a few more minutes and the wagons would be off. But at this unlucky moment shells began to fall on the gun side of the road, and close to where I was standing. Wherever I looked, spouts of earth or mud were leaping up. A man standing near to me was scratched by a fragment of shell, and the teams were on the road still. It was a nightmare situation

70

and I thought Ramsden's wound, slight as it was, needed a dressing. 'Sergeant Denmark,' I called, 'come here quickly!' He turned round, with a face of thunder. 'Who's taking charge here, are you Sir, or am I?' he said. It was a terrible moment. I, an officer, had given an order to one of my men and he had not obeyed me. It seemed to me that I should never again be able to hold up my head in the battery.

In fact, the situation was under control. Ramsden had licked and sucked the back of his hand which was no longer bleeding, the shellfire stopped, the last round of ammunition was carried across and safely put away, and I saw the wagons being driven away as I walked back to Lancer Farm.

But I was utterly miserable, I had failed in a crisis, I had not known what to do, I should never again be able to give an order. I was wretched all day. It was particularly disappointing because I had thought I was getting on more successfully with Sergeant Denmark since being in action with the battery. If Edward had been more friendly I think I should have told him the whole story and asked his advice. But I was afraid this would only lower me still further in Edward's opinion. What could I do?

Then I made up my mind. I knew that another load of ammunition would be coming up later in the day, and when it came I would go outside, go on to the road where the wagons were. Sergeant Denmark was sure to be there, he was always there whenever there was a job to be done. I would show him that I was not afraid for myself, that I did care about the battery and wanted to share in whatever danger there might be.

I had to wait a long time It was not until we had finished our dinner that the wagons came. Then, without a word to either of the others, as though I was only going to relieve myself, I went outside, out of the dug-out, round the nearer shell-holes, and jumped down on to the road. The night was comparatively quiet. Some shells landed in the château garden, but none on the road while I was outside. The wagons were about a hundred yards away and I walked up to them. The drivers all seemed in good spirits. 'Get a bloody move on,' I heard one say to the gunner who was unloading his wagon,

71

'Ah don't fancy bein' stuck in this place all t'flickin' night.' I had not seen Sergeant Denmark yet. Then I saw him, and he saw me.

'What are you doing here, Sir?' he said.

'I just wanted to make sure everything was all right.'

'Don't be so daft. Officers have got their own responsibilities. But there's nowt in unloading wagons and putting ammunition away. Anyone can see to that.'

I was still lingering. 'Now that the rain has stopped,' I said, 'we'll be able to strengthen those shelters a bit.' I knew it was the first thing Edward wanted to do, to sandbag the roofs and walls of the flimsy shelters where the men were sleeping.

'Don't be so daft,' Denmark said again. 'How do you think it's going to help us or anyone else if you go asking to be hit?' His voice was still gruff, but there was no anger in it now, and I understood that he had been nearly as worried and anxious as myself in the morning. Then I went back to the dug-out and slept well, far better than I expected to. It was all right.

We did not always sleep all through the night. I woke one night at about two o'clock, the hour when courage may be at its lowest, and heard heavy shells falling very close. Eight-inch, I thought they were. They were coming over one at a time at intervals of about a minute, and the dug-out shook at each explosion. Strong as it was I knew that it could not protect us from a direct hit from one of these, and I lay in silent fear as I heard each shell rushing towards us through the night. A terrifying explosion followed and I pressed myself against the wall. But it had missed us, it had fallen on the other side of the road, where A and D Batteries were, they were having a worse time than ourselves. After each explosion I started to count. If I could get to two hundred it would probably mean that the enemy battery had finished for the night and no more would be coming. But I never got beyond one hundred and fifty before I heard the scream of the next on its way. This screaming sound was more frightening than the explosion, there was a fiendish malevolence in it, and it seemed to be coming straight at me.

I thought I was the only one awake and envied the others. Then I heard Josh's voice. 'For God's sake!' he said, 'give us a light someone, and put on the gramophone. Let's see if we can drown the sound of those sods outside.'

There was a candle beside my bed, stuck into an empty bottle. I lit it and got up, and wound up the gramophone. I put on our Gilbert and Sullivan record, the others would not let me play it on ordinary occasions, they said it was too loud and that they did not like that classical stuff, but its loudness was an advantage now. I realised that everyone was awake, servants and signallers too, each of us had been envying the others for being asleep, now we were all talking at once.

Then I put on Solveig's Song, another favourite of mine, but that was too much for Josh. 'Oh, for Christ's sake, take her off!' he cried when she was on her top notes. 'She sounds just like one of them herself.'

We were all talking, but Josh talked most. 'Does anyone want to hear my candid opinion of the War?' he asked. He told us without waiting for an answer. Then he told us his candid opinion of Staff Officers and of all the people at the Base or on the Lines of Communications. 'They're the real bastards,' he said. 'Pinching all our grub and not knowing what sound a shell makes! And wouldn't I just like to be one of them! Inland Water Transport! That's the thing for me in the next war.' By exaggerating his own fear of shells he turned them into objects for laughter, we were all laughing before he had finished and before the shells stopped.

I did not know when they stopped. I fell asleep again. When I woke up my candle was burnt out, the gramophone had run down, one or the servants was making tea, and a signaller was folding up the gas curtain over the entrance, letting in the daylight and comparatively fresh air.

'Morning, Josh,' Edward said, as soon as he saw he was awake. 'Had a good night? Sweet sleep and happy dreams?'

'Blast you and your happy dreams,' Josh said. 'I'll tell you how I'm going to spend today. There's a lot of rubble outside and we've got plenty of sandbags. I'm going to put so much stuff on top of this place that it will keep out even one of those seventeen-inch brutes that Frank says are always following him about. I shall need a lot of men to help me. Just see to that, will you, as soon as you've had your breakfast.'

73

9

Outside Bank Farm

The shellfire never stopped. Day and night it went on. But no further infantry attacks were made for more than a fortnight. The rain had drowned the battle.

At last the weather improved. The Great Offensive was to be resumed, the infantry would attack again, the artillery would go forward. We received our orders, all the minute details, the same creeping barrage, the exact times, the position to which we should advance. And each battery was to supply a Forward Observing Officer to go up with the infantry. 'Whose turn is it?' the Major asked. It seemed to be mine. He sent me down to the wagon lines for two days.

I was aware of a feeling of anxiety. This would be the most responsible as well as the most dangerous task that had been given me, but I was reasonably confident that I could do it. I had been under shellfire so often that I thought I had nothing more to learn about that; I knew what it was like, very disagreeable, but endurable. And I had been up to the infantry front line, within sight of the enemy, across the battlefield where the dead men were still lying. Yes, I could do it. It would probably be a very difficult day, I should be glad when it was over. But when it was over, I should be able to feel that now I had done everything, there would be no worse experience for me to go through.

I was not going alone. Vernon of B Battery was coming with me. He was the officer from South Africa who had joined the brigade on the same day as myself. I liked him very much; there was no one whom I would have preferred for my companion. We made our plans together on the afternoon of the day before the Attack. Zero Hour was at 4.20, but we had no responsibility for the first wave of the attack, two other officers were going out for that. Our responsibility began at $Z+100$ minutes when the second wave was to go through. By that time we were to be at Bank Farm, in our present front line, we were to follow up from there, finding out how far the infantry had gone and the strength of the opposition against them. We were to lay out a telephone line forward from Bank Farm and send all our information there. Another telephone line from Bank Farm to the rear was already in operation, its maintenance was the responsibility of the Royal Engineers, not ours.

'It all seems fairly straightforward,' Vernon said. It was his first time also as Forward Observing Officer on the day of an attack, and we went over our plans again, to make sure that we knew all the times correctly. Then we arranged to meet at two o'clock on the road by our batteries.

It was a dark night, but our eyes soon grew accustomed to the darkness, and it was quiet. This time in the morning was often the quietest part of the day. At first we were on a road, we were to call in and see the Colonel on our way up.

Colonel Richardson and Cherry were asleep, but they woke up and welcomed us in a very friendly manner. The Colonel put on his spectacles and blinked at us amiably from behind them. I think he disliked sending us out into danger as much as he would have disliked going there himself.

'Information is what we want,' he said to us. 'All that you can get: where we are, where the enemy is, any strong points that are still holding out. You supply the information, we do the rest. It's not only our own guns, we can get the heavies behind us to fire at anything that's too big for us.'

He and Cherry were both very encouraging. It was going to be a much better show than last time, they said, all the enemy pill-boxes had been pounded to bits. But I remembered what Jack had said, that anyone could be optimistic if he lived in the kind of place where they were. Then they wished us good luck and we went out into the night again.

Now we had to leave the road, we had to clamber over trenches and shell-holes. This was where the two front lines had been a fortnight earlier. We could only go very slowly, our signallers had more than a mile of heavy telephone wire

75

to carry in addition to all their ordinary equipment, which included two lamps. We had eight signallers, four from each battery, my Bombardier Turner was in charge of the party, and we also had four men from a trench mortar battery who had joined us at Brigade Headquarters. They were to act as runners if we could not get our information back by telephone.

We had decided not to try to reach Bank Farm before Zero Hour. It would have been difficult to find our way there in the darkness and there was no advantage in going so far forward. We would stop at the top of the ridge and wait there until it was light enough to pick out Bank Farm. We should have plenty of time to get there before Z+100.

We stopped in an old German trench, part of their reserve line before the battle started. It was only half past three, we were in good time. Vernon closed his eyes and dozed off, but I felt no desire for sleep. Now that we had started I was no longer aware of anxiety, only of excitement. I was looking forward to the day. The deep trench was full of other soldiers, but I did not know who they were or what they were there for, no one was speaking.

At a little before 4.20 we went outside and climbed half way up the parapet so that we could see. Then there was a roar of guns behind us, we checked that our watches were right, and looked in front to see what was going to happen. All the enemy rockets were going up, and over our heads red points of light sped through the darkness, our own shells rushing to burst on the German lines. We could see the flashes of their explosion, and nearer to us German shells began to fall. But the noise was much less than it had been when I was standing in the middle of the guns.

Daylight slowly came. Now we could see the battlefield. In front of us the ground sloped down very gradually for about half a mile. Then began to rise again, a little more steeply. The Steenbeke was in the bottom, a few stumps of splintered willows marked where the course of the stream had been. That was our front line, or it had been at 4.20. That must be Bank Farm, a little to our right, just across the stream. By this time our infantry ought to be on top of or over the ridge on the other side, but it was not yet light enough to see any movement there. We could see the pill-boxes on the top: Iberian, Delva Farm, Gallipoli. They did not look as though they had been pounded to bits, but perhaps it was all right, it was very hard to see. They were just low blocks of concrete, not more than three or four feet high. Bank Farm was another. There were about a dozen in sight altogether, some ours, some his; or they had been his, they ought to be ours now. There was nothing else to see. Nearer to us some of our wounded were already coming back, their white bandages showed out clearly in the surrounding greyness.

It was time to be off. The enemy was putting down a heavy bombardment in front of us, but most of the shells were falling in the same places, and before leaving the safety of the trench we worked out a zig zag course for ourselves, so as to avoid them. We tacked across the sea of death. In a straight line we had only a thousand yards to go, but it took us nearly an hour. The sun came up above the horizon in front of us as we were going. The long summer day had begun.

Up to this time everything had gone well for us. We had arrived at Bank Farm, we were in good time, our party had suffered no casualties, we had not even been particularly frightened, none of the shells had fallen close to us. Now we were to go up the slope on the other side and find out where our infantry had got to.

But we never went beyond Bank Farm.

I saw one of our machine guns firing from a trench at a short distance on our right. If the attack had been successful there ought to have been no German within range of a machine gun from here by this time. And machine guns were generally fired over open sights. If those gunners could see the enemy then he could see us. Vernon also had seen the machine gun firing and had drawn his own conclusions. 'We'd better find out what's happened before we go any further,' he said.

We separated. There were plenty of people to ask, but no one could tell me much. No one that I saw was doing anything, everyone looked as though he was wondering what to do, except those who had already decided to do nothing. Then I saw Tommy Rust, one of A Battery's officers, and a friend of mine. I knew he had come up the night before, he was acting as liaison officer to the infantry, he would be able to tell me. He was a very smiley person as a rule, but he did not smile now. It had been all right at first, he said; then the infantry had met a counter-attack; and the pill-boxes had shot at them from behind. I understood him to say that some of our men had come back, but he could not stop with me, he was going somewhere with the infantry colonel.

I saw Vernon looking for me and went to where he was. His information was much the same as my own. 'It seems as though they haven't been pounded to bits,' he said. At that moment we saw some men coming down the slope in front of us. They didn't seem to be walking properly, they looked as though they were walking in their sleep. I saw Tommy's Colonel going out to them. 'Come on, lads!' I heard him say. 'I'll take you up there.' They took no notice of him, they just walked past him. He called to some of them by name. 'Come back with me, I'll lead you there myself, don't let the Regiment down.' He was an oldish man, his voice was pleading, not commanding. They went on walking. Some of them stopped when they got to the trench at Bank Farm, others crossed over it and went on up the hill. It was the first time I had seen men who were finished. 'We must tell Brigade what's happened,' I said.

'We can't,' Vernon said, 'there's no line.'

'Is it down?' I asked. I thought he meant it had been cut by shellfire.

'I don't think it's ever been up.'

'What do you mean?'

'I don't think there's ever been a line back from here.'

So there was nothing we could do. The attack had failed, our men were back where they had started. All our guns would be doing no good at all. Adding on a hundred yards to their range every few minutes as though the infantry were close up to the curtain of fire. But the infantry was back here, what was left of them.

We sent back one of our runners, but I did not feel sure that he would ever find his way to Brigade Headquarters. At the best it would take him an hour and he would certainly never return to us. We sent a second one a few minutes later, I made him go a different way.

Then I went to find Bombardier Turner, he might be able to suggest something. 'I'll try a lamp,' he said, when I had explained the situation to him. 'The sun's good,' he said. It was a satisfaction to find someone who knew what he could do and was going to do it, and his voice was the same as on any other day. Within a few minutes he came to tell me that he was getting an answer from the ridge behind us and that we could send messages through to Brigade Headquarters. We sent one immediately. The attack on our front had failed, we said; the infantry was back at Bank Farm; there might still be some parties of our men up on the ridge in front, but the pill-boxes were still held by the enemy.

It was not yet seven o'clock.

All this time we had been under fire. Shells were falling over the whole area, in the valley of the little stream, on the side of the hill where we had come from, up to the crest behind us, which was as far as we could see. But the shellfire was not particularly heavy and Bank Farm was receiving no more than its share of attention. In front of us we could not see so far, the ground rose more steeply, we could not see the top of the ridge, or the pill-boxes, which had been the cause of our failure. But the bottom of the shallow valley, where we were, may have been under enemy observation from somewhere. At any rate the shelling suddenly became worse, I was aware that shells were falling all round us.

'I don't like this, we'd better get down,' Vernon said.

But there was no place to get down in. There were two pill-boxes at Bank Farm, both very strong, but one was the head-quarters of the infantry battalion, the other a dressing station. There was no room for us in either. There was a trench at the side of the pill-boxes, but it was so wide and shallow that it was almost useless for protection. But in one place there was a low wall beside the trench. It was on the wrong side of the trench, the non-German side, so that one was completely exposed on the side from which the shells were coming, but it was better than nothing, and we made our way to it quickly. Half a dozen other artillery officers were already there, sheltering behind it. We joined them, crouching down at the bottom of the shallow trench, with the wall behind us. I was at one end, Vernon was next to me. I did not know where our signallers were, I hoped they had found some sort of shelter, but the shelling was too heavy to go and look for them.

I hoped it would only last for five or ten minutes, concentrated shelling was usually over in a short time. But it went on. Some of the shells fell very close, and they were big ones. I flattened myself against the earth and the wall. The dressing station was about twenty yards from me, on my right, I was the nearest one to it. There was not room inside for all the wounded men who had been brought there. Some had to be left outside, or were taken outside if they were hopeless cases. They were a long time dying. Unconscious they may have been, but they heard the shells coming. Their crying rose to a scream as they heard the sound of one coming, then fell away to a moan after the shell had burst.

I learnt to distinguish the different crying voices. Sometimes one stopped, and did not start again. It was a relief when this happened, the pain of the crying was unendurable. But there were new voices. The crying never stopped, the shelling never stopped.

Then I stopped noticing the crying voices. I was conscious only of my own misery. I lost all count of the shells and all count of time. There was no past to remember or future to think about. Only the present. The present agony of waiting, waiting for the shell that was coming to destroy us, waiting to die. I did not speak to Vernon, Vernon did not speak to me. None of us spoke. I had shut my eyes, I saw nothing. But I could not shut my ears, I heard everything, the screaming of the shells, the screams of pain, the terrifying explosions, the vicious fragments of iron rushing downwards, biting deeply into the earth all round us.

I could not move, I had lost all power over my limbs. My heart throbbed, my face was burning, my throat was parched. I wanted a drink, there was lime juice in my water-bottle on my back, but I could not move my arm to pull it towards me. I could think of nothing but my own suffering. Still the cruel shells screamed in their fiendish joy, still the sun beat down on us.

It stopped. I did not realise that it had stopped, I do not know how long I had been lying there, thinking that it still went on, but I heard a voice speaking and I opened my eyes. A newcomer had joined us, an officer in the Engineers, he was standing by the other end of the trench, furthest away from me. To my surprise I recognised him. It was someone who had been at school with me, five or six years before. I had not liked him. One of the masters had called him Fairy because he was so clumsy and the nickname had stuck. He still looked clumsy. There was a smear of dried blood down one of his cheeks. He kept on touching the wound with his finger and then looking at his finger to see whether the bleeding had stopped.

'Lot of wounded up at the top,' he was saying. 'Any of you fellows coming up with me?'

None of us spoke.

'They're crying,' he said. 'I've heard them.'

Still no one spoke.

'We can get a stretcher,' he said.

One of the others spoke for us all. 'We've got our own job to do,' he said.

He waited for another minute, standing there, fingering the course of the blood down his cheek. None of us moved. 'No one coming?' he said. Then he went away. I did not see where he went to, I never saw him again.

We got out of our hole.

'I feel awful for not going with him,' Vernon said to me some time later.

'It wasn't our job,' I said.

'I know,' he said. 'I feel awful.'

At some later time he tried to go up the hill by himself. If I had known he was going I might have gone with him, he did not tell me until he returned. He had not gone very far, he said; they were sniping. 'I hadn't the guts to go on,' he said. While we were standing talking together the back of his hand was scratched by a thin splinter of shell, he licked the place with his tongue and put on some iodine. 'If it had been a bit bigger,' he said, 'I might have got away.'

We couldn't go back yet, it was only twelve o'clock. But we were doing no good where we were, we could see nothing from Bank Farm, there was no telephone line, we were no longer even in lamp communication with the ridge behind us, Turner said there had been no reply to his signalling for some time past.

We waited. I saw that the other artillery officers were going back. Tommy Rust said there was no possibility of our making another attack that day, there was no one left to make one. If anyone did any attacking it would be the Germans, he said.

'Let's go,' I said to Vernon. 'Let's go back to the ridge, we can speak to Brigade from there.'

He agreed. 'We can always come back here if they want us to,' he said.

I don't think I could have gone back, I had a horror of Bank Farm. It was the most terrifying place I had ever been to, or imagined in a nightmare. I did not mind where we went, so long as we left Bank Farm.

We went back up the hill, not to the place which we had left at dawn, but a little to the left of it. That was where Turner had been signalling to, and we knew there was a line from there back to our batteries. We had to wait for some time when we arrived there, the other artillery officers were there before us, they were all telephoning to their brigades. But at last it was our turn and we got through to Cherry. I was hoping he would say we had been out long enough and tell us to come in. But he didn't. He said we had been quite right to come back on to the ridge, we could see from there, but we must keep a good look out for enemy movement; there was quite a chance of his launching a strong counterattack, we must report at once if we saw anything. And if nothing happened we could come in as soon as it was dark, he said.

Dark! It wouldn't be dark for another seven hours. He might as well have told us to stay there for ever.

We had just finished speaking to him. The telephone was inside a pill-box, the other officers had gone outside, we were looking at each other. There was the sudden scream of a shell, followed by a very loud explosion. Everyone was trying

82

to rush inside through the narrow doorway, there were screams of agony outside. 'Who is it?' we were all asking. It was Gladwin and Dearden, two of those who had been up at Bank Farm with us. Dearden was dead already, Gladwin was brought inside. There was a doctor in the pill-box and he went to where they laid him, but there was nothing he could do for him, he said. He just shook his head when he came back to us.

We went outside. It might be more dangerous out there, but I could not endure the moaning of the dying man, I'd had as much as I could stand for one day. Anyway, we had been told to look out for enemy movement.

We found a place about a hundred yards in front of the pill-box, and our signallers laid out a line to it from the telephone pit. There was a small patch of flat ground on which we could lie down and a shell hole close to it in which we could shelter if we had to. But we did not have to use it, no other shells fell close, the peace and stillness of a summer afternoon seemed to have descended on the battlefield.

There was peace behind the German lines also; I could see no movement anywhere. Down the hill to Bank Farm, up again on the other side. Somme, Gallipoli, Iberian—there they were, low grey slabs of stone in a desert place, like the huts of primitive man. And beyond that ridge there were other ridges, I counted three or four, there was grass on the furthest one. I could see grass and trees and red brick houses, the village of Passchendaele again.

Some way to the right, but almost due east of where we were lying, a grey obelisk stood out on a hillside. That was Zonnebeke church, all that was left of it, the village had gone, only this one wall of the church remained. My eyes followed the line of the railway coming out from Ypres. It crossed the low ground on an embankment, then went into a cutting near the ruins of the church and disappeared from sight.

Once during the afternoon I saw half a dozen Germans coming down the hill past the church. I saw them only for a moment, I called to Vernon, I moved my glasses away from them and when I looked again I could not find them. Neither of us could see them. They had so utterly vanished that I wondered if they had ever been there. The sun beat down on us, there was no shade anywhere on the battlefield, there was no variety of colour, just the hard brown of sun-baked mud.

'I think it's almost harder to bear on a day like this than when it rains,' Vernon said.

I did not want to eat anything, my mouth was too dry and when I took a drink of lime juice out of my water bottle it was warm and bitter to the taste.

We took it in turns to close our eyes for ten minutes.

We stared at Zonnebeke church.

We spoke to Cherry again. As there was no sign of a counterattack developing we thought he might tell us to come in, but he only said 'Keep on watching.'

Another hour passed, but when I looked at my watch it was only twenty minutes. I hoped it might have stopped, but Vernon's agreed with it.

Oh, the misery of this desolate land!

'Did you ever imagine it would be like this?' Vernon asked.

'I've forgotten what I imagined,' I told him.

The sun was hardly moving.

'If we'd come away from Bank Farm sooner we should have been the ones who were standing outside,' Vernon said.

The same thought had occurred to me.

'It fell right in the doorway,' he said.

I had a sudden idea. If I rang up the Major he might suggest to Cherry that we had been out long enough, Cherry would take more notice of him. I succeeded in getting through to him.

'Where are you?' he asked.

I told him.

'Anything happening?' he asked.

'Not now,' I said.

'What sort of a day have you had?' he asked.

'Not very good,' I said nothing more and he rang off, but sometime later Cherry spoke to us. 'Anything happening?' he asked.

We told him that everything seemed quiet.

'Well,' he said, 'it's only seven o'clock, but I should think it would be all right for you to come in now.'

We did not delay. Our patient signallers would have stayed up there without protest for the rest of the day, and night as well, but now they moved with alacrity. Bombardier Turner, who was a serious-minded young man, gave me a quick passing smile. It was the first time that day I had seen anyone smile.

We came to the crest, we did not once look back, now we were going down on the other side. We could see where our guns were and the ruins of Ypres in the saucer below us. The rays of the sinking sun gave them a strange beauty. The sun had been with us all day, in our eyes as we were going forward to Bank Farm, in our eyes again now as we came down to the Bellewaardebeke.

'This time last week I was in Piccadilly Circus,' Vernon said. 'You're lucky, you've got your leave still to come, you'll forget all about this when you go home, it will only be a bad dream.'

I suddenly felt an extraordinary affection for Vernon, I wanted to have him always at my side. Together we had been down into the valley of the shadow, together we had climbed a little way out of it, a little way out of the pit. But we had nothing else to say to each other. We parted on the road, in the place where we had met, just eighteen hours earlier. I watched him till he was out of sight, then turned and walked towards my own mess.

Frank and the Major were finishing their dinner when I came into the dug-out. I smiled at them, there was nothing else I could do, I did not want to talk.

'What's it been like?' Frank asked.

'Put some food inside yourself,' the Major said. 'Eat first, talk afterwards, that's the rule.' And he poured out a whisky for me.

Afterwards I did talk. I had never talked so much, words poured out of me. The faces of the men who had been dead for a long time, the demoralised soldiers coming down the hill, and the poor old man of a colonel who had tried to rally them, the intensity of the shellfire, the cries of the dying, the death of the two gunner officers when we came back—it all rushed out of me. And the sun all day, glaring, burning, indifferent. The sun had added to my wretchedness.

'We've all had to go through it,' Frank said when I had finished. The gentleness of his voice surprised me. The Major wanted me to tell him more about Bombardier Turner. 'Was he under fire when he was using his lamp?' he asked. I did not really know, I had not been with him all the time. 'I think we were all of us under fire most of the morning,' I said.

'He did very well,' the Major said. 'His lamp brought us the first information that the attack had failed. If it hadn't been for him we should have gone on firing into the blue till kingdom come. Not just ourselves, but all the other brigades. That's the worst of a creeping barrage. We might as well have been chucking oranges at Fritz for all the harm we were doing him.'

He said he would put him in for a decoration, and some weeks later Bombardier Turner was awarded the Military Medal. But before the award came through he had been badly wounded, one of his legs had to be amputated. I wrote to him in hospital in England to tell him about the award, and he seemed pleased to have been given it. 'You got it for me, sir,' he wrote back. But how could a medal make up for the loss of a leg? He never walked again without crutches, and he was a young man.

'You seem to have done pretty well yourself,' the Major said. But I had not told them about my paralysing fear in the shallow trench, nor anything about Fairy. For a moment I thought of telling them, telling them I had been so frightened that I could not move and that I had been afraid to go up to the top of the hill. But I said nothing more, I had said enough. Now that the first rush of words was over I no longer wanted to talk about what had happened. I wanted to think about it, but I would not talk about it again, neither to my friends, nor in my letters home. Vernon knew, but no one else should ever know the extremity of the fear to which I had been reduced.

But several days later, happening to find myself alone with

Frank I mentioned to him that a sapper officer at Bank Farm had gone up to the crest in front in full view of the enemy in order to bring back some of our wounded, and I asked him whether he thought it was the right thing to do.

'No, most certainly not,' he said. 'It needs at least two men to carry one wounded, and the chances are that they would both be hit before they brought in a single man. What's the good in that? It's crazy to do that sort of thing in the middle of a battle; you've got to wait till it's over.'

Mathematically he was right. Losing two men in an attempt to save one was obviously of no use, but it made no difference to my belief that I had failed, and I should like to have asked Edward what he thought, his answer might have been different, I believed. But I never asked him. What made it harder for me to forget was that I had always thought myself a better person than Fairy in nearly every way.

The Major sent me down to the wagon lines on the morning after the attack, Jack coming up in my place. I was glad to go down. I wanted to be alone for a few days, and it was easier to be alone at the wagon lines, I had a tent to myself. I wanted to try and find out why I had been so afraid, and what I could do to prevent its happening again.

For fear of that sort was horrible, debasing, abject-making. I had never been afraid like that before. I had been rather less afraid than most others, not more afraid. I had felt frightened under fire, but I had remained myself. At Bank Farm I had ceased to be myself, I had become another person, one out of whom all courage had been poured away. It could not be just fear of death, I thought. For I had always known that I might be killed, everyone at the front must know that. I might have been killed on half a dozen previous occasions.

It seemed to me that my fear must have been due to a combination of circumstances. First, there had been the faces of the dead men. I had seen them before, but never so many. One couldn't avoid seeing them, one was given no warning. You took a step forward, and there the body was, lying on its back at the bottom of a shell-hole. My friends did not seem to mind, they were tougher than I was. Vernon said he just felt sorry for them. I did mind, I couldn't help it. I should have to try and make myself more familiar with the sight. Until I had done so, it would continue to make me feel sick. It made no difference whether they were Germans or our own people.

Then there had been the sight of our men coming back down the hill. They looked awful too. They were alive, they were moving, but more like puppets than men. There was no expression on their faces, it was as though they had lost their souls. And in the moment of seeing them I realised that our attack had failed utterly. It had been a worse failure than the first day of the battle, we had not gained a yard on our part of the front.

And then the concentrated bombardment. It had started suddenly, before I was prepared for it. Always before it had been no more than half a dozen shells, it had been all over in a minute or two; or else I had been inside a dug-out. At Bank Farm we had been practically lying in the open, and it had gone on for about a couple of hours. If I had known beforehand that it was going to happen I could have braced myself to bear it. Another time I should know. I should know that one always might come under fire on the day of a battle, out in the open, without a place to run to.

If these were the reasons for my fear it seemed to me that I need not suffer again in the same way. I had been warned now. I should be ready for that kind of fear the next time. It did not matter being afraid of death. Everyone was. Everyone wanted to live, not to die. Death might come, it had been hovering very close to us at Bank Farm. But there was nothing one could do to prevent its coming, or make it less likely. Feeling afraid did not lessen the risk. So what was the use of feeling afraid! All that suffering, and no advantage. The only sensible thing to do under shellfire was to find the best place that was available and stay there. Wait for the shelling to stop. It was simply a matter of endurance, like enduring any other pain.

I felt triumphant, I thought that I had conquered fear. Lying in bed in the morning in the peace of the wagon lines, hearing the sound of gunfire distantly, and nearer at hand the rustling of leaves outside my tent and the stamping of feet of horses,

I thought that I should never feel that terrible fear again and a great weight was lifted from my mind. Life was beautiful. I loved it. I did not want to die, but if death had to come I would not let the fear of it spoil the rest of life beforehand.

I felt so confident that I wanted to return to the line at once, to come under fire and show myself that I was not Bank-Farm afraid. I almost looked forward to the next time that I should have to go out as Forward Observing Officer on the day of a battle. I would do nothing foolish, I would take no unnecessary risks, if or when the shelling started I would take cover at once and remain there till it was over. But I should not suffer as I had suffered that morning at Bank Farm, I had solved the problem of feeling afraid.

I thought I had conquered fear, but of course I was deceiving myself. I never conquered it.

Life went on as before.

The Major told us the war had lasted long enough and he was going to make a separate peace and take no further part in it. Edward could command the battery, he said. Edward would like that, and the experience would be good for him if he wanted to become a Regular after the war.

Edward was not present to hear these remarks. He and Josh were up at the guns by themselves. Jack had gone on leave, Frank and I were at the wagon lines with the Major. I had never heard Edward say that he wanted to be a regular soldier, but the Major said oh, he had often talked about it, and it would suit him very well, the army was just the place for a boy like Edward.

'The trouble about the war,' the Major said, 'is that it stops you doing all the interesting and worthwhile things.'

At that time of year, he said, one ought to be thinking about partridges, and he intended to start thinking about them. He had brought his shot-gun back with him after his last leave, and now he was going to use it. Every day he went out shooting in the fields round our camp. He was happier than I had ever seen him, he was hardly drinking at all. He was particularly pleased because Major Fraser of A Battery was down at his wagon lines also, and the two went out together. Major Fraser was an Old Etonian. 'He's shot all over the place,' the Major said. 'With all the swells. So of course he fancies himself.' What made the Major so pleased was that he was being the more successful of the two.

I thought that Edward and Josh had been left up at the guns for a long time and I suggested to the Major that I should go up there. I couldn't of course take Edward's place, but I could either relieve Josh or stay up there with both of them, thus lightening for each of them the amount of work there was to do.

'What's all the hurry about?' the Major said. 'We'll give ourselves one more day. Or even two. It won't do Josh any harm to stay up there, he's seen much less of the war than the rest of us. And as for Edward, he prefers being up there, he always has preferred it, he's not interested in horses, he can't find anything to do with himself at the wagon lines.'

He was mistaken. The next morning there was a rude and angry letter waiting for him on the breakfast table. It had come down from the guns during the night. Edward had been looking in his diary and had counted the number of days that he had spent in the gun line, and the number the Major had spent there since the beginning of the battle. He was doing three-fifths of the Major's work, he said, and all the captain's; the Major did damn all except enjoy himself when he was at the wagon lines, but he was drawing his major's pay all the time. Edward said with a good deal of rudeness that it had got to stop, there was to be a more equal division in future.

The Major laughed and showed us both the letter. 'Poor old Edward!' he said. 'Something's bitten him. Fancy keeping a diary so as to be able to count how many days you've done in the line. I wonder what's upset him. We shall probably find they've been playing poker with A Battery and have lost money. Ten to one that's what it is. Edward hates losing money, he's a bit close with his money, that's the only thing I have against him.'

He did not hurry. He went out shooting again in the morning, but after lunch he set off with Frank to walk up to the guns, leaving me to follow when the others came down. 'But if they're going into Poperinghe and you would like to go with them,' he said, 'tomorrow morning will be time enough.'

My sympathies were with Edward and Josh. Although he had been very nice to me I thought the Major was slack, and that he had behaved selfishly in staying at the wagon lines so long. But when the other two arrived I found that I was included in their resentment.

'Wagon line hero!' Josh shouted as soon as he saw me.

Edward was so angry that he did not speak to me. He and Josh went into their tent and began changing their clothes at once, I could hear their angry contemptuous voices. They were going into Poperinghe and I had been looking forward to going with them. I had not been there since the day at Bank Farm. I could not afford to go with the Major, he spent too much money there; and Frank did not go at all, he was saving up. But it was very clear they did not desire my company, they would not have accepted it.

'Wagon line hero!' Josh shouted from the tent when he saw me outside. 'If there's one type I can't stand,' he said, 'it's the sort of fellow who tries to shirk out of all the danger.'

I might have looked in my diary, but I knew without looking that my score was bigger than his, and he had not done a Bank-Farm yet. But it was no use trying to argue with them. 'Wagon line hero'—was all Josh would say, and Edward said nothing. They did not reply to my 'Cheerio!' as they were going off. They went in one direction, to Poperinghe; and I went in the other, up to the line.

I felt very disappointed. I did not mind what Josh called me, I was accustomed to his mockery. He was altogether unlike myself, and I was certain that I could never win his good opinion, I did not especially desire it. But Edward I admired more than anyone else in the brigade, and in the last few weeks, since the beginning of the battle, he had become much more friendly. But now I had lost all that I had ever gained with him.

'Well!' said the Major, when I arrived at the battery position. 'How are they? have they got over their childish display of petulance?'

'They called me a wagon line hero,' I said.

'Don't pay any attention to them,' he said. 'Everyone knows that's what Josh would like to be himself, a wagon line hero. He gives himself away by calling you one. But Edward has no right to talk to you in that way. He can say what he likes to me, but I won't have him making offensive remarks to my young officers, I'll give him a good talking-to the next time I see him.'

'Actually, it was only Josh who called me a wagon line hero,' I said. 'Edward wouldn't speak to me.'

'He'll be feeling better in the morning,' the Major said. 'There are some very good qualities in that boy, but he has no control over his temper. That's the only thing I have against him. He's always working himself up into a state about something or other of no importance. I've spoken to him about it, I wanted to help him. But it's no use, Master Edward always knows better than anyone else.'

He had left a hare that he had shot at the wagon lines for their lunch on the following day. He believed in heaping coals of fire, he said; turning the other cheek, all that sort of thing.

'I expect they'll be too proud to eat it,' Frank said. 'They'll probably give it to the servants.'

'Oh, don't you believe it,' the Major replied. 'They may tell us that's what they've done, but Josh is as fond of a good meal as anyone else, and so is Edward. You won't find either of them giving away good food.'

We had a very good dinner ourselves. There was a partridge for each of us, chipped potatoes and bread sauce, and two fresh vegetables. Medley had excelled himself, he enjoyed giving us a good meal as much as we enjoyed eating it. Major Fraser from across the road had been invited to come and share it with us.

Afterwards the two majors talked. They had seen the world, they did not just talk about shells and the bloodiness of war. Listening to them I almost forgot that I was sitting in a dug-out by the Bellewaardebeke, that shells were falling outside, and that to-morrow or the day after I might have to go up to Bank Farm again, or Plum Farm or Apple Villa or some other evil place. I was very happy. It was a great deal more enjoyable to be sitting here where I was welcome, listening to the interesting conversation of the two majors, with Frank putting in an occasional remark, a great deal more enjoyable than I should have found it at Poperinghe with Edward and Josh, listening to their grumbles about the war and all the rest of us.

Major Fraser stayed till after midnight, and the Major went on talking for a long time after he had gone. 'The great thing,' he said, when we were going to bed at last, at some time between one and two o'clock, 'the great thing is to remember that we're civilised human beings. We know this, and we try to keep up a decent way of living. This is where we are more fortunate than people like Edward and Josh, who can't see further than their own noses. I'm sorry for them.'

He was awake and about again soon after seven o'clock, he never seemed to need much sleep. 'Six hours for a man, seven for a woman, eight for a fool,' he was fond of saying. He was still in very good spirits when he came back from visiting the men.

'I've a good mind to stay up here always,' he said. 'Those other two will soon get tired of kicking their heels at the wagon lines, and then they'll come begging us to change places with them.'

'Not Josh,' Frank said, 'he won't come. You'll live to be as old as Methuselah if you have to wait for him to come.'

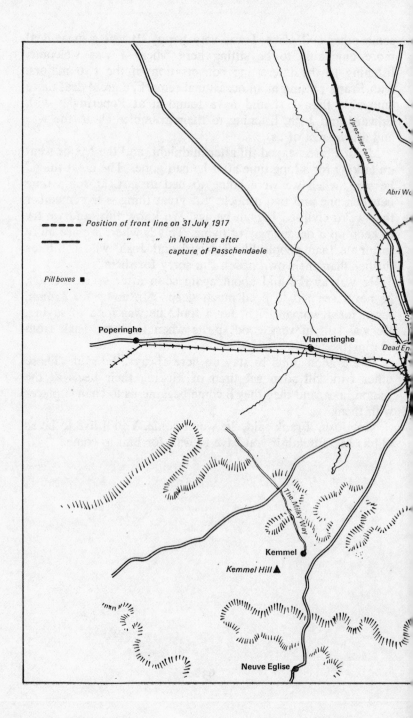

Position of front line on 31 July 1917

" " " in November after
capture of Passchendaele

Pill boxes ■

Ypres-Iser canal

Abri Wo

Poperinghe

Vlamertinghe

Dead En

S

The Milky Way

Kemmel

Kemmel Hill ▲

Neuve Eglise

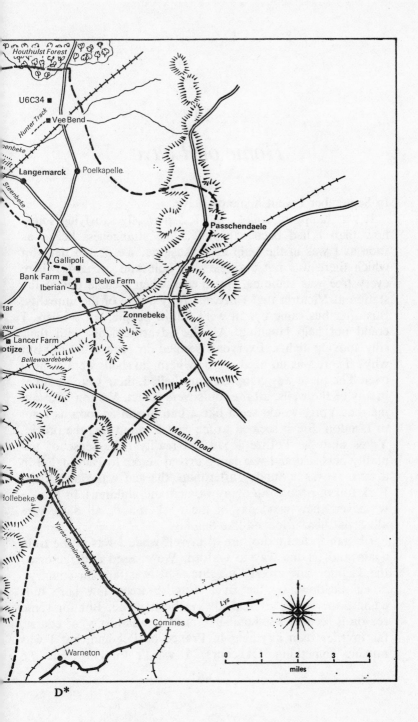

Houthulst Forest

U6C34

Hunter Track

Vee Bend

nenbeke

Langemarck Poelkapelle.

Steenbeke

Passchendaele

Gallipoli

Bank Farm

Iberian Delva Farm

tar

Zonnebeke

eau

Lancer Farm

otijze

Bellewaardebeke

Menin Road

Hollebeke

Ypres-Comines canal

Lys

Comines

Warneton

0   1   2   3   4
miles

D*

10

Home on Leave

In September I went home on leave.

It was happy of course, but less perfectly satisfying somehow than I had been expecting. The strangeness began as
soon as I was in the train at Folkestone. We passed fields in
which there was not a single shell-hole and orchards where
every tree was standing. But it was when I came out of the
station at Victoria that I became fully aware of the unreality.
Bus after bus came by, all were full of people, not soldiers. I
could not help laughing. All the advertisements with their
silly moving lights. Everyone seemed in such a hurry. But
why? There was no need to hurry here, no shells were coming
over. The place was completely unshelled, there were no holes
in any of the walls, all the roofs were intact. Vernon had told
me that Ypres would seem like a bad dream as soon as I got
to London. But it seemed to me that London was the dream,
Ypres and the Potijze Road the reality. The sense of unreality persisted as I was being driven across to Paddington in
a taxi. It was a Sunday afternoon, the sun was shining, the
Park full of people. So many women and children! In France
we never knew what day of the week it was, all days were
alike, but here it looked like Sunday.

I began to feel more sure of myself when I was in the train
again and on the way to Oxford. We crossed and recrossed
the Thames, and crossed it again. This was familiar country:
green meadows by the river, English trees, low bare hills
against the sky. This had always been home. But for some
reason it seemed less home-like now. It was lovely, of course,
far lovelier than anything in France or Belgium, but I was
missing something. Of course I wasn't thinking that the

96

Potijze Road was my home now, that would have been absurd. But it was odd that I should be thinking so much about the others, and odd that I should not be going to see any of them for ten days.

It was wonderful when I arrived at home. Wonderful to feel so much happiness, and to give it, wonderful to be so perfectly loved. But the feeling of strangeness remained. On my subsequent leaves I was more successful, but on my first one I never completely succeeded in adjusting myself to the change. I was happy. I enjoyed the quietness, the luxury of sheets on my bed, the absence of fear. Above all I was happy in the love of my parents, but I had to try and conceal from them that I was missing something, that I could not put the men of C Battery out of my mind.

My parents wanted me to tell them everything about myself, everything that had happened since I went out, but there were some things I could not tell them. I could not make them understand. I could not tell them that I had become a different person myself. They might not have liked my new friends. If they could have understood, they would have liked them, but how could they understand when they had not been out there!

I enjoyed being with my young sister. She laughed with me, she did not ask me questions about the war, there was nothing she wanted to know about it. For her my leave was no more than a brother's home-coming, but for my parents I had returned from the gate of death and was due back there in less than a week's time.

And all the time I was thinking about the others, wondering whose turn it was to go up to the O.P. and what the shelling had been like today.

I took off my uniform and put on my own clothes, thinking that this would help me to remember where I was. But when I was in the town, a soldier, a corporal in the Oxford and Bucks, stopped to ask whether I didn't want to be out there, with all the other lads. I do not remember my reply, but a true answer would have been that I was there, not here in the middle of Oxford.

My parents took us, my sister and myself, to Brighton for

a few days. They thought the sea would help me to forget, but I did not really want to. Juliet, my pretty young cousin, who lived there, would have made a fuss of me, she always wanted to have me with her, and she asked me questions about everything. Was I always in danger? Had I ever been afraid? What was a battle like? Were Belgian girls as pretty as English ones? But she did not really want to know the answers and I did not want to tell her. She was talking to me because I was an officer in uniform, the only one there.

Then we returned to Oxford, and I to the front a few days later on the 8.50 am from Victoria, my parents watching forlornly on the platform until the train was out of sight.

11

Out at Rest

I found all the others at the wagon lines when I got back to Vlamertinghe. The Brigade had just come out of action.

'Thank God, you've come back on the right day!' Josh said as soon as I walked into the mess. 'I'd have cheerfully murdered you with my own hands if you hadn't.' He was waiting to go on leave himself, and could not go until after my return.

'You're lucky, you've done well for yourself,' Edward said. 'We're going out to Rest tomorrow.'

'We've had a pretty hectic time while you've been away,' Jack said. He told me the names of our casualties.

'We made another attack,' Frank said, 'but we stayed in the same place. How's Oxford?'

The Major wanted to know what shows I had seen in Town. I hadn't seen any. I told them I'd had a marvellous time, I'd enjoyed every minute of it. I did not say I was glad to be back, I did not know whether I was. But at any rate it was a relief to be only one person again, just a part of the B.E.F., no longer a mixture of two quite different people.

Josh rode off the next morning as soon as it was light. The leave train left at ten o'clock, but he had heard that the railway station at Poperinghe was being shelled by a long-range gun, and he wasn't taking any risks, he said. 'You won't find me sitting in a train that may be shelled,' he said, 'not with a leave warrant in my pocket.' He was going to join the train at a place further down the line, he was prepared to ride all the way to Boulogne if necessary.

'What's the betting that we never see him again?' the Major said to the rest of us at breakfast. 'I'll lay anyone odds of five to four against his ever coming back. Who'll take me? Fifty francs to forty against our ever seeing him again in this country.'

Edward took him.

We marched out to Rest after breakfast. We went a long way back, so far that we were almost out of range of the sound of the guns. We were billeted on a farm, we had a comfortable room in the house for the officers' mess, but our tents were in an orchard. By day so much was happening, and there were so many other noises on the farm, that we hardly noticed the sound of gunfire. Only in the early morning, when it was louder, we heard it; and sometimes again at night as we were falling asleep, and the noises of the day had ceased. The War was still there, that distant murmuring of the guns was no more than a threat and a reminder, but we should have to go back there again, we had only escaped for a little.

But for the moment we had escaped.

Football, battery sports, riding—these were our occupations now. I learnt that we had a very good football team, we played matches against the other batteries and one or two other teams that were resting in the same area, and did not lose any of them. I was now as proud of my battery as any of the others, and as sure that there was not a better one in France. None of the officers was nearly good enough to play in the football team, but we all took a keen interest in our matches. Sergeant Appleby, happily recovered from his wound, came into the mess in the evening, and he and the Major discussed the composition of our team before every match. Appleby was a beautiful player, he had played professionally before the war, I had never seen such skill. We could not lose, I thought, when Appleby was playing for us, so calm and confident and always with a smile on his face. Some of our other players were rough, tempers sometimes flared, there were arguments with the referee, but Appleby checked every outburst at once. He was indisputably in command. Even the Major took second place in the battery on the day of the match.

Riding was the Major's chief interest now. He told us on the first evening that he would expect all his officers to come

100

out with him before breakfast every morning. Frank refused. He said that he had to risk his life every day in the line, but he was not going to do so when we were out at rest. He lay in bed jeering at Jack and myself, because he said we hadn't the courage to follow his example. The Major told us he was disappointed in him. The men liked to see their officers riding and jumping, he said; Frank thought it did not matter, but he was quite mistaken. 'I should say it's one of the things that matters most for an officer,' he said. 'Men will always follow an officer who's got the sporting spirit.'

Edward usually came with us, but Jack and I went out every morning, and often we were joined by some of the officers from the other batteries. Frank had been right in what he said about me, at first I should have preferred to stay in bed, I was frightened of following where the Major led us. But my riding improved. In England, in the riding-school, I had learnt how to hold on as well as most of the other cadets, and we had been taught the various tricks—jumping, and vaulting back into the saddle while running along beside our cantering horses. But it was the horses that had the skill.

Now for the first time I began to enjoy riding, and to make my horse go where I wanted her to go. I was not always successful, she was very powerful, sometimes she ran away with me still. But I was growing very fond of her, she was a beautiful light bay, and when officers in other batteries came to praise her good looks or her jumping I felt as proud as though the credit belonged to myself.

At first I fell off nearly every morning, but always after a fall I would find the Major waiting for me, and he would tell me what mistakes I had made. 'You rushed that one,' he usually said. 'You didn't hold her in, you've got to take charge, you know—you're the man.' Sometimes he would say it was her fault, not mine. 'Look at her face when you get up,' he said. 'If she's got a dirty face, then you needn't blame yourself.'

Before our rest came to an end I was hardly falling off at all.

The Major was making a steeplechase course, we all knew

there was to be a great race meeting, open to all the brigade, before we went back into the line. The Major himself was a good rider, but not as good as he would like to have been. Major Cecil, our former captain, was a better one. Edward rode with more courage than skill, Josh was too heavy, Jack and I were both too nervous to make good riders.

'You'll enter for the race, of course,' the Major said to me. 'You ought to have a very good chance on that big mare of yours, there's nothing she can't jump.'

I did not want to go in for it, the jumps were frightening, but I seemed to have won the Major's good opinion and did not want to lose it. There were to be half a dozen races altogether, but the Officers' Open Chase was the big event of the day. Everyone from the Colonel downwards would be there to watch, and I dreaded the thought of making a fool of myself in front of the whole brigade. The Major himself was one of the favourites.

Josh had come back just in time for the great day, only a week later than he should have been. He had been ill, he said, but none of us believed him. So the Major had lost his bet with Edward, but for the moment nothing mattered except the race. Jack scratched his entry, he said Dolly had injured her fetlock, but no one else had noticed her limping. I spent a very uncomfortable morning, as nervous as on the evening before a battle. But the Major said a little nervousness beforehand was not a bad thing, it meant that all one's powers were alerted.

Josh was making a book on the race. Frank worked out the odds for him. Sergeant Denmark told me he had put ten francs on me for the honour of the Left Section.

'I didn't think you were so daft,' I said, using his own favourite word.

'You needn't be afraid of anyone on Theodora,' he said. 'She's all right,' I agreed, 'it's the man on her back who's no good.' He told me to hold her in before taking each jump. 'Don't let her rush them,' he said.

The race was a disaster for the battery. The Major came off at the second fence, he said one of the other riders had bored him as they were coming up to it. I went round the first time safely, but then fell off just as I was beginning to think how easy it was and when I was running third or fourth, not far behind the leaders. Edward finished the course, but was unplaced. The race was won by an outsider. Major Cecil, the favourite, finished fourth. Josh cleared five hundred francs, more than a month's pay, he was the only one of us to derive any satisfaction from the race.

It was an unpopular result in the battery, and the Major was in a black mood that night. 'Just like he is after a battle.' Jack said. 'We might as well be up in the line.' He and I had come out to our tent in the orchard because he was making himself so disagreeable in the mess.

But presently Josh came out to us and told us that we could go back. 'He's all right now,' he said.

What had really upset him, Josh said, was the fact that he had made so much money. And he hadn't liked having to pay Edward fifty francs because he had returned from leave. 'He thinks Edward nobbled me,' he said. 'Silly chump! If he had told me beforehand what he was going to do, I might have done something about it.'

But everything was all right now. Josh had said he was going to celebrate, he was going to spend all his winnings on a tip-top dinner for us all in Cassel or somewhere. We would paint the place red, he said. 'That's bucked him up,' Josh said. 'Now he's beginning to see the funny side of this afternoon. It was damned funny.'

I had other lessons to learn besides riding.

Jack asked me one afternoon to ride with him into the little town. He wanted to do some shopping, he said; and he had found a place where there were two very pretty sisters. I was not interested in what he said about pretty sisters, but I knew that I should enjoy his companionship on the ride.

I changed my mind, however, when I saw Suzanne. She was very beautiful. I had not expected anyone so attractive or so young. She looked about sixteen. In England a girl of her age would have been at school still, and as shy as myself; we should have found nothing to say to each other. But Suzanne began talking at once, she talked to me, I did not have to think what to say to her, she spoke in a mixture of French and English which sounded more enchanting than any language I had ever heard; and when she smiled at me I could think of nothing except how to make her smile again. I moved closer to her, I could not take my eyes off her face.

She was talking to me about myself. How cruel it was, she said, that one so young should have to fight. I was a brave English soldier, but all English soldiers were brave. She did not know what would have happened to herself and her family and all the people of France if it had not been for the brave English soldiers.

I asked her to speak more slowly. How I wished that my French was better: It had seemed a waste of time at school to learn French, now I could see the reason for learning it. She laughed at my pronunciation of her language, she spoke with exaggerated slowness, smiling between every word, her eyes shining. I was enraptured by her loveliness. And she was still talking to me about myself, as though I was the only person that mattered to her. We had come back to recover ourselves after the trenches, she said; she could see how much I had suffered, my suffering showed in my eyes; but I was brave, I pretended it was not difficult; she did not know how anyone was able to endure so great hardships and dangers.

Jack meanwhile was talking to the elder sister. She was not at all pretty, I thought; and I wondered that anyone should want to look at another girl when Suzanne was in the same room, but he seemed content. Jack was better at French than I was, he was talking quite easily, but I was not listening to what he said. All my attention was centred on Suzanne. She was talking at her ordinary speed again, and I understood only a few words of what she was saying. But it did not matter. I only wanted to look at her. I smiled at her, pretending that I understood what she was saying. She smiled back at me. There was nothing else in the world that mattered but that she should go on smiling and looking at me.

Before we left I bought an expensive silk handkerchief from her. I did not want it. There was nothing in the little souvenir shop that I did want, a handkerchief would do as well as anything else. I wanted to buy something from her, I thought that our hands might touch when she gave it me.

But a much more wonderful thing happened. She put the handkerchief into an envelope for me, and as she did so a little box slipped down and fell on to the counter between us. I moved to pick it up and put it back in its place, she gave me my envelope at the same moment, and a lock of her hair brushed against my cheek as we moved. It was only for an instant, it was so slight that I might not have known anything had touched me, but it was a lock of a girl's hair. The girl was Suzanne, who was more beautiful than anyone I had ever seen.

I was not conscious of anything else. We left the shop. We were riding back to camp. Jack was talking, but I did not know what he was saying. Suzanne's hair had touched my cheek. The world was more beautiful than I had ever imagined. Nothing like this had ever happened to me before. A bird was singing, but the bird was my own joy. A girl's hair had touched me. My cheek had felt the electric touch. Sing, sing for joy.

'We must go there again,' Jack said, when we had dismounted and our grooms had led the horses away. 'You seemed to be getting on well with Suzanne. There's sometimes an old dragon of a mother in the shop, but we were lucky this afternoon.'

I did go there again, but I went alone and I waited for an evening when all the others were out. Then I took the battery bicycle, I did not want to have my groom with me, no one should know where I was going, and I rode along the dusty paved road to the little town.

I was lucky, or so I thought, for I found Suzanne alone in the shop. This was more than I had dared to hope for, and I had been wondering how to get her to myself. She remembered me and seemed pleased to see me, she smiled again and spoke in her lovely mixture of English and French. She was so beautiful that I would have spent all the money I had in buying bits of lace or postcards or candlesticks that I should have no use for in the line.

But after a few minutes her manner changed. She stopped smiling, she answered my questions monosyllabically, like an English girl, she moved further away from me. She was much cleverer than I was. I did not know what was in her mind, but she knew what was in mine. Girls are quicker than boys, they learn to look after themselves, they are not so defenceless. All my knowledge came out of books, she knew what life was, and how to deal with a situation that was not to her liking.

I realised I was doing badly this time, and I lost my head. I made the mistake that the Major was always warning me against—I rushed my fence and took a bad fall in consequence.

'Mademoiselle,' I said appealingly, 'we are going back to the war.'

I was lying to her, we were not going back, there was no talk of our going back yet, but I wanted to win her compassion, I wanted so desperately to kiss her.

I moved towards her and tried to put my arm round her, but she was much too quick for me, she ran away before I could touch her. There was a door leading out of the shop into the rest of the house, and she ran to it and stood there, holding the handle of the door, ready to open it if I took a step towards her.

And she would have opened it, she would have called her sister or the old mother Jack had told me about. I was utterly defeated. I was terrified of an angry woman. I could endure shellfire, but not the contempt of a girl or the anger of her mother.

But I tried once more. I had heard Jack say it was the easiest thing in the world to kiss a girl. It was what they wanted, he said. They wanted to be kissed even more than we wanted to kiss them. I moved one foot towards her, I so longed to kiss her or at any rate to touch her hand or her hair.

'Mademoiselle,' I said, 'Je suis triste.'

But she made no reply, she only shook her head and put a finger to her lips.

I went out of the shop. I was still hoping she would call me back or at least say good-bye, but she made no sound or movement.

I felt angry and ashamed of myself, not for having tried to kiss her, but for having failed.

I had completely failed. I had got into the habit of rather looking down on Jack. I liked him very much, but I thought I was a better soldier than he was, and therefore a better man. But he could do what I was unable to do, and at that moment there was nothing in the world I so much wanted as to kiss or to have kissed Suzanne.

How I wished I had taken a lesson from Juliet in Brighton!

I had a wretched ride back to camp. Only a few days ago I had been so ecstatically happy, a door had been opened and I had seen a new heaven and a new earth; now it had been slammed in my face and I no longer believed in the beauty on the other side of the door. My pride was bitterly hurt, and I was afraid of being laughed at. For the others would certainly get to know what had happened, Jack was sure to go to the town again and Suzanne or her sister would tell him, and he would tell the others.

Josh was the one whose mockery I particularly dreaded when he got to hear. He was always making fun of my youth and innocence. 'Here comes our cock virgin,' he sometimes said. Once he had introduced me in this way to two stranger officers he had invited into the mess. 'Take a good look at him,' he said, 'he's the only one in France.' And at the thought of the mockery I should have to endure I wished I had never seen Suzanne. She had given me a moment's happiness, but it was not worth the price I should have to pay for it.

But the story never became known. Either Suzanne did not tell, or Jack kept quiet about it, and I was grateful to whoever it was. Gradually the bitterness of my disappointment lessened, and I was glad that I had seen Suzanne. I still remembered my extreme unhappiness at the moment of leaving her, I saw her so clearly standing against the door, unsmiling, ready to open it, with her finger against her lips. But I remembered her beauty also, and the exhilaration of the moment when her hair had touched my cheek. I had been angry with her, I thought she had given me nothing, but I was mistaken—her gift was one that I never lost.

Our Rest went on. We never had such a long one again. And up in the line so did the battle. The September attacks were more successful than the August ones had been.

'They seem to do better without us,' Frank said.

'Someone should tell them so,' said the Major, 'then perhaps they'll leave us here for the duration.'

I applied for four days leave in Paris, and it was granted.

12

Paris

'I only know one reason for going to Paris,' Josh said, 'why do you want to go?'

'I want to see the sights,' I said.

'At your age you ought to know nothing about them,' he mocked.

Two other officers in the brigade went there at the same time, Major Fraser of A Battery and Jamieson, a big Australian in B. Major Fraser was a very good officer and the Colonel's favourite, but he kept aloof from the rest of us. He stayed at the most expensive hotel in Paris, Jamieson and I were content with the second most expensive one. But we all three met together for a drink once a day.

Paris intoxicated me.

It was unlike any place I had seen or thought of. The leaves were beginning to fall in the boulevards, but it was still warm enough to sit outside, drinking coffee or sipping an aperitif, and watching the world go past us. This was a world with which I was altogether unfamiliar, and yet I felt at home there, more at home than in London, in spite of all the blue uniforms of French soldiers. Blue uniforms and well-dressed attractive women, there was so much colour, none of the drabness I had seen in London.

Jamieson helped me to feel at home, he gave me a sense of security in this new world. He was several years older than myself and up to this time I had seen little of him. I knew that Vernon liked him, and he and Edward had the reputation of being the best poker players in the brigade, though they were very unlike, Edward young, impulsive, enthusiastic, Jamieson

109

impassive and unsmiling. Both were equally ruthless, that was the resemblance between them, and they were calm in the moment of danger.

Now I made friends with Jamieson. He spoke in a drawling voice that probably showed where he came from, but he never talked about Australia. Nothing ever surprised him, nothing aroused his enthusiasm, but he missed nothing.

'They're all in the profession,' he said disparagingly, noticing my look of admiration for some women who had just passed us.

I was astonished.

'I thought women of that sort always looked old,' I said.

'Not in a place like this,' he replied. 'They wouldn't get any clients if they did.'

'But they look nice people,' I protested.

'Why shouldn't they be? They're doing a useful job.'

'What happens to them when they do grow old?' I asked.

He shrugged his shoulders. 'Some make good marriages and settle down,' he said. 'Some of them don't.'

I was interested and puzzled. I had never seen prostitutes before, or not knowingly, or only in towns down the line— Havre or Boulogne—where they certainly did look old and were without any physical attraction for me. If all prostitutes were old and ugly, then one could just feel sorry for them, nothing else. But if these women were prostitutes, the matter was not so simple as I had supposed.

Two very attractive women came into our restaurant one evening and sat down at a table near us. One of them was especially beautiful, I had noticed her before and was pleased to see her again and that she should have happened to come so near us. I looked at her as often as I could, trying not to be seen to do so. She was not like Suzanne, she was older, her face lacked Suzanne's gaiety, her eyes did not smile. I did not want to touch her or make her smile at me, my feeling for her was altogether different, I just wanted to look at Helen of Troy, I thought.

'She's one of them,' Jamieson said.

'Oh, she can't be,' I said. I had never seen anyone who looked more queen-like.

110

'I ought to know,' he replied. 'I have the best possible reason for knowing.'

The next morning he told me that Major Fraser had laid a proposition before him. It concerned myself, he said. The Major had a friend in Paris, Jamieson told me; and if I liked, she would provide me with a companion who would be perfectly safe. The Major thought I might not realise how great the risk was; that was why he was making the suggestion; he stressed the fact that I need feel no anxiety whatever with his friend's friend. And the cost would only be two hundred francs.

Only!

Two hundred francs was a lot of money for a junior officer. But I had spent so much already that another two hundred would not have made much difference, and there would be nothing to spend money on when we went back into the line. But I had no desire to accept the offer. To want to kiss Suzanne was one thing. I had seen her, I knew how attractive she was. But to go to bed with a woman I had not seen was a different matter altogether. I never considered the possibility of acceptance.

'Please thank him,' I heard myself saying, 'but I don't think I want to.'

'I didn't think you would,' Jamieson said.

But I did buy some postcards of girls to pin up on the earth wall beside my bed when we went back into the line. I knew my parents would have been distressed to see what I was doing and this made me feel uncomfortable, but the pictures would help me to sleep and that was important.

We left Paris on the evening of the following day. I was not sorry to go, I had had enough of it. Another day or two of such luxurious living and I might not have wanted to return to the hardship and danger of the line.

On our last afternoon we visited Napoleon's tomb. I was impressed by the number of other soldiers there, and by the variety of their uniforms—there seemed to be men from every one of the allied nations. In my new enthusiasm for France I thought it was right that men should have come from every far corner of the earth to pay respect to the greatest of

111

all soldiers. But Jamieson, the Australian, interrupted my thoughts: 'It was a good thing we beat him,' he said, 'they're an unstable lot.'

Major Fraser returned before us. The brigade had gone back into the line, we were all recalled by telegram, but Jamieson and I arranged to miss the afternoon train and hoped that the Major would have done the same. We had some difficulty in finding where the brigade was, but none in explaining about the train, Jamieson was always convincing. The brigade had not gone back to the same part of the line, we were further north, on the left flank of the British Army, the French were next to us, then the Belgians, then the sea. A different part of the line, but the same battle, the same mud, the same prospect of casualties—another attack was to be made in a few days.

The others were all in low spirits when I returned, and the mud at the wagon lines was awful. Frank was depressed because there had been no mail for three days, Jack and Josh because we were returning to the line, to fight more battles. But I sensed that something had happened while I was away to account for the general gloom. No one was in the mood to talk, the Major had gone home on leave, Edward was up with the guns by himself. Josh asked me if I was still what I had been, and I told him of Major Fraser's suggestion, expecting he would call me a damned fool for not accepting. But to my surprise he was indignant with Major Fraser. 'That's not the right way at all,' he said, 'he ought not to have suggested it.'

I was astonished. I suddenly realised that Josh liked me, liked me as I was, in spite of all his mockery. For a moment I thought of telling him about Suzanne, I wanted him to know that I was as much attracted by a pretty girl as anyone else. But I didn't. I wondered, however, what he thought was the right way. I liked Frank's way. He was miserable because there had been no letter for him for three days. I thought I should enjoy having a similar reason for misery.

13

Back in the Mud

Josh and I rode up to the gun line the next morning. Edward was as taciturn as the others had been. But there were two special officer-tasks for the battery, he told us: a dawn-to-dusk job at the O.P. and a 24-hour liaison duty with the infantry.

'Better toss up,' he said.

'I don't mind doing the O.P.' Josh said, 'If you would prefer the liaison.' I ought to have suspected that he had obtained fuller information, that he already knew the O.P. was nearly three miles behind the line and the infantry battalion head-quarters practically in it. But even if we had tossed and I had won I might have chosen the liaison duty. All the others could kiss girls, I couldn't. I had to show myself that there were some ways in which I was better, that I was less afraid of danger.

I set off with two signallers immediately after lunch. On this occasion and always afterwards when I had to cross over the wastes of death I divided the way into four parts. The guns were in a reserve position at Abri Wood, where they did no firing, and from there to the Steenbeke, a distance of about a thousand yards, it was comparatively simple. We came under fire at once, but no shells fell dangerously close, and there were other soldiers in sight all the time and shelters to run to if necessary. The second stage, from the Steenbeke to the Broenbeke, was worse. It was always difficult getting across the Steenbeke. There were a lot of guns in the shallow valley, the enemy knew this and shelled it by day and by night. One had to wait at the top of the declivity, wait for a lull, and then go quickly. The third stage, after the Broenbeke, was easier in one respect because there was a duckboard track laid over

113

or round the shell-holes. I tried not to look at the dead men. There had been heavy fighting in the last ten days, we had made a considerable advance, but at great cost. The ground was littered with the bodies of the dead, Germans, English, French. 'They're all here,' one of my signallers remarked, 'you can take your choice.' How many others there may have been under the water in the shell-holes I could not tell, but there were very many that I did see. A few were still recognisable in death, they might almost have been sleeping. I was grateful to them for looking alive.

The last stage was the worst of all, though there was less shellfire as one came closer to the line. This was always the part I dreaded. We were in view of the enemy, his eyes were on us. It was quite flat, there was no cover of any kind, there was no one else in sight, there was nothing to see. A few pill-boxes, thousands of shell-holes, full or half full of water. Nothing else close at hand, but in the distance, a mile away, was a dark line between the sky and the bare desert of mud. That was the Houthulst Forest, all of which was still in German hands. That was where the enemy eyes were.

I always had a feeling of being watched, that a German gunner had his gun trained on a certain point of the track and was waiting for me to get there. So strong was the feeling that sometimes I left the comparative security of the duck-boards, where at any rate one was safe from drowning, and walked across the mud.

We came to our journey's end, the headquarters of the infantry battalion holding the line. It was in one of the captured pill-boxes, Louvois Farm. The French had named many of these. The liaison officer's duty was to stay with the infantry, make friends with the officers at H.Q., bring fire to bear on any targets they gave him, and sometimes to investigate a complaint of short shooting. It was good for us, the gunners, to see how much better off we were, and nearly always I got on very well with all the officers I met from the Colonel downwards. There was always a telephone line at H.Q., so that I was in touch with Cherry and could pass on to him any message from the infantry colonel.

My 24-hour tour of duty passed slowly, but without incident;

I was relieved by another officer in the brigade in the early afternoon, and was always much happier going down than I had been coming up. Crossing the Steenbeke I met Major Fraser. The old Etonian was the best-dressed officer in the brigade, perhaps the only one who took any trouble over his appearance, but now he was unshaven and haggard and mud-splashed from head to foot, but he smiled at me wanly. 'I think we've met before,' he said, 'a place called Paris.' He told me he was on his way to a meeting of battery commanders with Colonel Richardson.

Edward also had gone to attend the meeting, and while we were by ourselves Josh told me what had happened while I was in Paris. There had been another flaming row between the Major and Edward. 'No one seems to know what it was about,' Josh said. 'I told them both they were behaving like silly school kids, but I couldn't stop them, and the very next day there was this order about medical students being allowed to go home to finish their training, and Edward at once said he was going. He wishes now that he hadn't, he doesn't want to leave the battery, but he'd be a fool not to go. His brother in the R.F.C. has just been killed, so he thinks he ought to go home for the sake of his parents as much as for himself.'

14

Vee Bend

A few days later we were given our preliminary orders for the attack.

On X-Day we were to establish a new O.P. in a much more advanced position than the one Josh had been to and on the following day, the day before the attack, C and D Batteries were to move from Abri Wood up to the Broenbeke. A and B were not going so far forward, they were going to the Wijdendrift, nearly a mile behind us.

Edward told me to be responsible for the new O.P. I was to get up at half past six and find my way to it. A telephone line had already been laid, Cherry had told him, but there might be a few breaks in it.

I set off immediately after breakfast. My signallers mended forty or fifty breaks, under fire all morning. Then they told me it would be quicker and more satisfactory to lay out a new line instead of patching up the old one. Soon after midday they had completed the task and I was at 'Vee Bend', the new O.P. It was not far from Louvois Farm, where I had gone to do liaison duty, a little further back, but within sight of it, and facing the sinister Houthulst Forest. There was a good pill-box, that was what mattered. I had eight signallers with me, two of my own and two from each of the other batteries. One was wounded before the end of the day.

I found some confusion when I returned. The Colonel had changed his mind. Because of Edward's youth he decided to send B Battery to the Broenbeke and to give us the supposedly easier position further back. Edward was furious. 'I won't have anyone saying I'm too young,' he said to the

116

Colonel, and persuaded him to stick to his original plan. But Frank, in charge of the wagon lines, a long way back and in communication only by mounted orderly, heard of the first alteration but not of the second. Thinking that the guns were to move a comparatively short distance he had sent out all the teams to bring back a big supply of ammunition. This had exhausted the horses and when he heard that the guns, after all, were to make the longer advance, he had ridden up to tell Edward that the horses might not be able to achieve it. He explained that he had acted from the best of motives because he knew how much ammunition the guns would require. Edward was angrier than ever. 'You've no business to think,' he said to Frank, 'you take your orders from me. I promised the Colonel I could get my guns up and now you're letting me down.'

I was sorry for Frank. Jack told me that Edward had been bloody rude to him. But Frank said Edward's anger was justified, although it was not his fault. Getting the guns up to the right place was the only thing that mattered.

However it was all right. Frank came up again very early the next morning with the limbers and firing battery wagons and teams of eight horses instead of six. The mud was appalling. But the horses were rested and whenever we came to a particularly bad place the gunners got down and pulled on the wheels, the horses strained on their traces, and soon after twelve o'clock the guns were in position by the side of the Broenbeke, ready to fire, teams and wagons were on their way back and we had not suffered a single casualty. All the way along we had passed abandoned wagons. Some had been destroyed by shellfire, others had skidded into the swamp at the side of the road and could not be pulled out. I saw some unfortunate mules being shot because they could not be got out.

We had a quick meal and then Edward said he wanted me to take him up to the new O.P. so that he could register the guns. On our way there he told me we were to provide a Forward Observing Officer for the attack on the next morning. He was to be at the O.P. before Zero Hour, and it would have to be myself because I was the only officer who knew where it was. I was fed up. I thought it was time Jack or Josh did something, everything was being put on to me, one of them could have come with us now to find out the way to Vee Bend. Besides, I knew it would be a dangerous job and I had a particular reason for not wanting to go into danger at this time. We were all superstitious and someone had lit three cigarettes with one match a day or two before. He had tried to light four, but the match had burnt his fingers and gone out. My cigarette had been the third. I had told myself that if I could survive three days I should have expiated the bad luck, but tomorrow would only be the third day. Moreover, it would be exactly three years since the death of my brother, and that was the sort of trick fate liked to play, to have two brothers killed on the same day. We got up to Vee Bend during a lull, but the enemy began shelling again at once. I wanted to take cover inside the pill-box, but Edward was in a hurry to do the registration. If we waited it might be too dark to see where our shells were bursting, he said. The registration was done and we started to return along the duckboard track by which we had come up. "Hunter Track" it was called. Almost at once we heard an aeroplane behind us. It was a Boche, he was flying low above the track, firing his machine-gun.

'Oh hell,' said Edward. 'Damn and blast him!'

Edward was frightened. I had never seen him frightened before. I was so surprised that I did not immediately follow his example and drop into one of the shell-holes beside the track. 'Get down, you damned fool!' he said. We lay very still, pressing our faces to the earth. I heard bullets singing through the air and plopping into the mud. The Boche flew out of sight, then turned round and came back again, still firing. 'Where are our bloody airmen?' Edward said. 'Why the hell do they let the Boche have it all his own way?' He supposed they had all gone back to get their tea. But neither of us was hit. For some reason I was not especially frightened, perhaps because I was angry with Edward, angry for putting all the jobs on me, angry because he was going away, it would be like a brother leaving the family.

We returned to the Broenbeke together. There I read very

carefully all the orders that concerned myself for the following day, before going back to Abri Wood where, at any rate, I thought, I can be sure of a good night's sleep before I set off. I was frightened now, and very tired.

But I hardly slept at all. Zero Hour was at 5.35. I told the signallers to call me at two o'clock. But I was uneasy, I was afraid of oversleeping, I kept my boots on to prevent myself from being too comfortable. Gas shells were falling outside, they made an altogether different sound from high explosive. What a damned nuisance, I thought, we shall have to wear our masks. That will make us slower and it will be harder to see. It was a relief to hear the signaller outside groping his way in the darkness. 'Five minutes to two, Sir,' he said, raising the gas curtain, 'and there's gas about.' I got up at once and we left within a few minutes. The shellfire had stopped, but there was a strong smell of mustard gas and we had to put on our masks. It was drizzling. I should have to wear my heavy coat and I knew it would make me sweat like a pig and tire me. In front of us as we walked, the sky was red and this helped me to keep direction. It looked as though one of our airmen had found something inflammable behind the fringe of the Houthulst Forest.

Halfway up I was to meet the other F.O.O. Garnett of A Battery was coming with me. A and ourselves were rivals. Each of us thought our own the best battery in the brigade, and we took some satisfaction in disparaging their officers, except Major Fraser whom everyone liked and admired. Garnett, we said, was a medal hunter and not so brave as he pretended to be. He annoyed me as soon as we met. 'Checked all your equipment?' he asked. What the hell had it got to do with him whether I had checked my signallers' equipment? In our battery we knew our signallers could be depended on to check their own. Perhaps he thought that because he was in A he was in charge of the whole party, my signallers as well as his own. Then he said 'You know the way, I'm told. You lead, I'll follow you.' They all talked as though I was the only man in the army who knew the way to Vee Bend. Worse was to come. We started to talk about our job and it was clear to me from what he said that he intended to do all the going out to collect information, I was merely to send back his information. This was ridiculous, it did not require an officer to send back information over the telephone. I had seen nothing in the orders to suggest that he should be the only one to go out. We ought to take it in turns or else go together as Vernon and I had done at Bank Farm. But he said Major Fraser had made it quite clear to him that he alone was responsible for obtaining the information. Obviously, I thought, he wants to get all the credit for whatever we do, I was just to be the telephonist. Well, if he wanted to go out all the time I would let him, I had no wish to go out in front of Vee Bend, I had been there and knew what it was like.

When we came to Vee Bend I was dismayed at first to find the pill-box full of infantrymen who were obviously going to take part in the second wave of the attack. I had to explain that it was an artillery O.P. The Officer in charge offered to take all his men outside. 'Not bloody likely,' I said, 'there's room for us all.' I was certain the place would be heavily shelled as soon as our bombardment began. We waited inside until a few minutes before 5.35, then went out. Garnett said we must be prepared for any eventuality. He spoke to Cherry on the phone, told him we were in readiness and that he was going out in front as soon as it was light enough to see. He told me that the Colonel had said it would be a good show, we had learnt how to overcome the enemy's defensive system.

The barrage opened behind us, the rockets went up in front, the German guns replied. Garnett went off to obtain his information and I waited outside the pill-box.

Some wounded men came past me, the walking wounded. They had nothing to tell. Then a few prisoners. Very few. Then I saw a Staff Officer going up towards the front line, a real Staff Officer with red tabs on his collar. I had never seen a Staff Officer so near the line on the day of a battle. Then Garnett came back. I had not expected to see him so soon, he had taken a telephone out with him and was to relay his information back to me. But his signaller had not taken enough wire, he said. It was strange that he shouldn't have checked it, I thought. He said that first reports were satisfactory, but enemy shellfire was heavy. I could have told him that it would be. Then he went out again.

I saw the Staff Officer returning. He came across to where I was standing and asked me if our telephone line was working. I told him that it was.

'Then it's the only one that is,' he said.

'We have good signallers, Sir,' I said.

He was not only a brave officer, but a very capable one, and he had found out more about the attack than Garnett had. I listened to the report he was making on the telephone, and it was clear to me that the attack was not going well.

Garnett admitted this when he came back for the second time. The conditions up there were terrible, he said. He had never seen anything like it. The mud and the water in the shell-holes! There were no trenches, there was no front line, he said. The men were just lying in shell-holes—some of them seemed to have stayed in their holes instead of going out to attack.

Not that he had been up to the front himself. He admitted that he hadn't. 'You can't get there,' he said. 'What with the mud and the sniping.' And it was very difficult to find out what was happening, he said, we had gained some ground but probably not very much. We each ate a bully-beef sandwich. Then he went out again.

He went out half a dozen times during the morning. Each time he returned sooner than before and stayed longer inside the pill-box before going out again. I was beginning to like him. I certainly disliked him less than I had at the beginning of the day.

'I'll go out next time,' I said.

He protested. 'I don't see why you should do my job for me,' he said. But there was no conviction in his voice, he was quite willing now to let me go instead. It was quieter, enemy shellfire was only sporadic by this time. If I went out once I should satisfy my conscience, I could find out for myself what was known about the result of our attack, and whether there was anything for the artillery to do. Then perhaps we need neither of us go out again, we could relax.

Taking one signaller with me I set out. There was a pill-box in front of us, about half a mile away. Garnett had not been there, but it was certain to be a headquarters of some kind, I should find someone there who could give me information. That was where I should go. Inside our pill-box I had forgotten my superstitious fears of the previous day, but they returned as soon as I came out and began to move across the dreadful and deserted waste. It was deserted, there was no living creature within sight. Between ourselves and the low concrete rectangular block I was aiming for there was nothing to be seen except mud, shell-holes, and water. We floundered through the mud, slipping, stumbling, trying to avoid the bigger holes and deeper pools, and with every step safety was receding, danger coming closer. All the trees at the edge of the Houthulst Forest had been destroyed, they were no more than gaunt stumps. No enemy could be hiding behind them but, beyond the stumps, the forest was darker, I just saw a dark mass. That was where the Eyes were, the Watching Eyes. All the time we were moving nearer to them, nearer, nearer. But it was the quiet time of day. Some of our own guns behind us were firing, I heard the sound of their shells passing overhead; and a few German shells burst within sight, but none fell near us.

Bending low, to make myself a smaller target, looking down for the best place to fall if I heard a near one coming, I began to hope. We were closer now to the grey block than we had been when we started. I could count on four or five seconds' warning, time enough to fall.

Four or five seconds! I got no warning at all. We were half-way across when it happened. I saw a hole opening between my feet, water and mud leaping away, I heard the scream of the oncoming shell and the blast of its detonation in the same instant. We were blown to the ground, muddy water splashed down on us from every side, but the swamp saved our lives, it smothered the shell's explosion, we were not hit. We got up and staggered on, neither of us speaking. I stopped under the wall of the pill-box and opened my mouth to speak, but no words came out, only meaningless sounds. There was a flask half full of neat whisky in my hip pocket, I took it out and swallowed a mouthful, then passed it to my signaller who did the same. It may have been a chance shell,

122

fired at random, but there were no others and I believe we had been seen by an observer in the dark forest, an observer in communication with a high velocity gun firing a shell that travelled as quickly as sound.

I went round the corner and into the pill-box. My voice was still not wholly under control, but my questions to the officers inside—the headquarters staff of an infantry battalion —were intelligible, as were their answers.

No, they had gained very little ground, and there was no possibility of their making another attack that day.

Yes, they could show me on the map more or less where our line was.

No, there was nothing the artillery could do for them.

Yes, their casualties had been heavy.

One of them offered me a drink, but I knew they would need all that they had. I should be going back when night came, they would have to stay.

We went back as we had come. Nothing happened to us. I had decided not to tell Garnett about our narrow escape from death. Everyone had narrow escapes, no one was really interested in those of another person, we always thought he was exaggerating. Garnett came out to meet us.

'My God!' he said. 'Are you all right?' He had been watching us from the back of the pill-box, he had seen the shell burst, we had been completely enveloped in its black smoke.

'It was like a miracle when you came out of the smoke,' he said. 'I should never have forgiven myself if anything had happened to you.'

He talked as though he had been personally responsible for our near obliteration. I was touched by his solicitude on my behalf. He insisted on my going inside the pill-box and sitting down. He kept on saying how selfishly he had behaved. I couldn't help thinking that his care for me gave him an excuse for staying inside the pill-box himself, but he had suddenly become human, now I could talk to him. I realised that he was not a medal hunter, he was simply a very conscientious soldier without much sense of humour. He admitted that he had been frightened nearly out of his life in the morning, I told him I had been so frightened that I could not speak. We agreed that we could not go out again, that our legs would not take us.

We were to stay out until dusk, but if I had been by myself it would have been dusk at half past four. I wanted to suggest to Garnett that we should go, but we stayed for another hour or longer. We stood outside together, watching the light fade over the dreary wilderness. 'There might be an S.O.S.' Garnett said. 'There often is after an attack, we may be the only people looking out for it.' But darkness came down, no lights went up, the battle was over—for that day.

But even then Garnett was reluctant to leave. 'There ought to be somebody up here by night as well as by day,' he said. 'I've a good mind to ring up Cherry and suggest it, and say that I'll stay here until he sends someone up to relieve me. There's no need for us both to stay, you go without me.'

I said that if the Colonel wanted the O.P. to be manned all night, Cherry would already have arranged for someone to come out. But he did not feel sure of this. 'They're slack, you know,' he said. 'They don't take their responsibilities so seriously as you and I would if we were in their shoes. They really need someone to ginger them up.'

I couldn't bear the thought of his suggesting that another duty should be added to those we already had, and in the end I persuaded him to return with me.

'I'll have a word with Major Fraser when I get back,' he said, 'and see what he thinks.'

We walked back in single file along the duckboard track, stopping when we came to the Broenbeke and separating, I to go to my battery, he to his at the top of the higher ground between the streams.

'I should never have forgiven myself if anything had happened to you,' he said again. 'I shan't forget today.'

I thought it was probable that I should not forget it either, but he meant that he thought I was almost good enough to serve in A Battery.

Edward told me that he did not need me up at the guns, and that I had better go back to Abri Wood. I should find Josh there also, he said; he wanted Josh in the morning, but I could stay there for another day and night. 'You've got some sleep to make up,' he said.

I could hardly get back to Abri Wood, I was nearly finished.

'Come on, old boy,' Josh said, 'there's a tiptop dinner waiting for us.'

For the first time in a week I enjoyed eating. I enjoyed sitting down. I enjoyed feeling safe.

'Now you look more like your mother's son,' Josh said when the meal was over. 'Scrape off some of the dirt, and she might recognise you.'

I fell asleep. Josh said afterwards that he and the servants had carried me to bed and then undressed me. I stayed in bed half the next day.

I was reading "Framley Parsonage" and enjoying it very much. It described such a peaceful existence. The hero put his name to a bill and got into financial trouble, but that could not be so bad, I thought, as being F.O.O. on the day of an attack. Putting your name to a bill—I could only guess what it meant, but I did know what the other was. And one day, please God!, we should return to a similarly peaceful existence, in which we had only bills to worry about.

But we had not yet come to the bottom of the pit, we were still slithering downwards, the battle was still on. I do not know when it began to have a name, "Third Ypres" or "Passchendaele". To all of us it was just *the* battle, the battle which had started on July 31st, was still being fought in the middle of October, and was to continue for another two or three weeks.

With the Major on leave and Edward taking his place in the gun line, and Frank in charge of the wagon lines, there were only the three of us—Jack, Josh and myself—to take the special duties, and every third or fourth day it was my turn to be liaison officer or to go up to the O.P.

15

The Broenbeke

Once I was liaison officer with a battalion of Grenadier Guards.

Was I a Regular soldier, was the Colonel's first question.

'No Sir,' I said.

Had I been at Eton, his second.

'No, Sir,' again.

He appeared to take no further interest in me as a person, but I was impressed by him and what I saw that night. The discipline of the Guards was very strict and their behaviour even in the line very formal. The attitude of men to their officers and of junior officers to senior ones was always correct. Their conversation was serious, I heard none of the flippancy or cynicism that I was accustomed to in our own mess, and somehow this made the war seem less futile.

I admired the Guards, but did not feel at home in their company.

The Guards Division was relieved during the night that I was up in the line with them. The Grenadier Guards went out, an English county regiment came in, and the difference was perceptible immediately. Now, everyone was talking at once, there was an atmosphere of warm-hearted bustling, lovable inefficiency; packs and gas-masks, revolvers and field glasses were thrown down anywhere. Now we were all amateurs who hated war, but knew that it had to be fought and would go on fighting until it was won.

The Colonel of the incoming battalion was going with his adjutant to visit his outpost line and I offered to go with him. But he shook his head. 'No, Guns! Why should you come?' he said, 'it's not your job, it's ours.' I liked being called

"Guns" by the infantry. There was an implication of mutual trust in the use of the word.

But I was pleased that he had not accepted my offer, I did not want to leave the safety of the pill-box. There were no trenches here, the so-called front line was nothing more than a set of unconnected shell-holes, each manned by a few men, existing somehow where they had been put until relieved after 48 hours. I was much better off than an infantry platoon commander of my rank and he was better off than the men under him.

On another ocasion, Louvois Farm (the infantry battalion headquarters) and Vee Bend (the O.P.) both played a part in the night's adventures. The infantry were not in direct communication with our Brigade Headquarters, they could not themselves ask for artillery help. This was why they needed a liaison officer. But I was told that Vee Bend was now manned by night as well as by day, and therefore messages could be signalled by lamp to Vee Bend and then on by the telephone line we had laid. Soon after dark, however, my signallers came to tell me they were receiving no answer from Vee Bend. I had Shortwood and Foster with me that night. They were the two signallers who had accompanied me on the first time I went out across the waste of death, while we were still at Lancer Farm. They had, as it were, held my hand on that occasion, had taken me out and brought me safely back, and always afterwards I was pleased when I knew they were coming with me. They were as much a single unit as Gilbert and Sullivan or Huntley and Palmer. One had a villainous face, the other a cherubic one. In fact, both were first-rate signallers and first-rate down-to-earth Yorkshiremen, the kind of men responsible for our eventually winning the war. I don't think either was decorated except in the memory of those who, like myself, had the privilege of serving with them.

Now they came to tell me they were getting no answer to their flash-lamp.

I decided to send both back to Vee Bend, to find out what was the matter. It was dark, but they said they would be able to find the way there but not to return to me unless I guided them by flashing the lamp.

They set off. I gave them three-quarters of an hour. Then I went outside again and, setting the lamp in what I believed was the right direction, I began flashing a succession of dots and dashes as I had arranged with them before they started.

They were away a long time. I began to feel anxious for them. They might have lost the way, they might have been wounded, they might not be able to see my lamp. German shells were falling at no great distance, but I did not feel anxious on my own behalf. I had something to do. That stopped me from thinking about the shells, even from noticing where they were falling. I knew that the lives of my two men might depend on me.

They came at last, suddenly out of the darkness. I had not seen or heard them until they were within a few yards of me. They were as pleased to be back as I was pleased to see them, and I gave each of them a mouthful of whisky from my flask. But their news was bad. There was no one at Vee Bend, they said, the place was deserted. They had reported to our Brigade Headquarters by telephone that we were not in communication, and Brigade had said they would attend to the matter. But I knew that it was another brigade of artillery, not ours, that was responsible for the night O.P. and whether or when Cherry would succeed in getting anyone up there was more than I could guess.

I had to go and tell the infantry colonel that I was not in touch with anyone. If he needed artillery support during the night I should not be able to obtain it for him. He was alarmed, and angry. If I couldn't do anything for them, he said, I might as well not be there. I tried to put the blame on the other brigade, he put it on myself, and I knew that he was justified in doing so—it was an artillery failure, and I was the only artilleryman present.

Luckily it was a quiet night. The infantry had no occasion to ask for artillery support and in the morning, though not until then, I was able to tell the colonel that I was now in touch with the batteries behind us.

The officers of this battalion of the Highland Light Infantry to which I was attached that night were more than usually friendly, and I wanted to regain their good opinion, not only for my own sake, but because it was the chief reason for our existence—to fire at the enemy when the infantry required us to.

I was very proud of being a gunner.

Edward proved a good battery comander while the Major was away. In spite of his youthful appearance the men trusted him. He could do nothing to lessen their danger or discomfort, but he cared, and showed that he cared. The valley of the Broenbeke was shelled day and night, but our good fortune continued. We had fewer casualties than A and B Batteries in the supposedly safer position behind us, and fewer than the other brigades on the Broenbeke. There were guns all way along the road by the side of the stream.

The stream! The road! How misleading words can be! The "stream" was a succession of mud-and-water-filled shell-holes, the "road" a causeway of shell-splintered planks, unfit for wagons of any kind. All our ammunition had to be brought up by pack-horse.

Edward was now my friend as much as any of the others. We shared a tiny pill-box at the top of the rise behind the guns. There were two, the signallers lived in the other, and we still had the good one at Abri Wood. There was no going down to the wagon lines at this time, but we took it in turns to go back to Abri Wood for a night's rest.

Then the Major returned from leave and took his place with the guns. Edward went down to the wagon lines, Frank came up. So for about a week there was an extra subaltern and that meant fewer duties for each of us. The Major immediately found a larger and drier pill-box. 'There wasn't room to swing a cat in Edward's place,' he told one of our visitors, 'if it had been a bit bigger we could have swum in it, the water on the floor was nearly deep enough.' But he praised Edward for standing up to the Colonel and refusing to go to the other position. 'You should always put your guns as low as you can,' he said, 'not on the top of a hill.'

130

I was told one morning there was a visitor in the mess who was asking for me, so I went down from my tiny box, wondering who it could be. The man was a captain in the R.A.M.C., I recognised him, his home in Oxford was near mine and he explained that his mother and mine had been talking together and had realised we were close to each other. He was medical officer to one of the other brigades by the Broenbeke and he had been told to look me up. I took out my case and offered him a cigarette. That was always the first thing to do.

'No, thank you, I don't smoke,' he said.

Then I offered him a drink—that was the second thing politeness required.

'No, thank you, I don't drink,' he said.

We talked for a few minutes about the Broenbeke, comparing casualties, agreeing that it was a terrible place, but I was not finding him easy to talk to, and presently he got up to go. I tried one more opening, for I thought he might have some advice to give me. 'Read any good books lately?' I asked.

'I don't have time for reading,' he said, 'but I always try to read a few pages of Homer at night before falling asleep.'

Then he left, I watched him walking down the hill and along to his own brigade.

'Who was that joker?' the Major asked, when he had gone.

'His name is Lawrence,' I said, 'and he's a brother of that fellow we were reading about in *The Times* who's always blowing up trains behind the Turkish lines.' Frank and the Major both knew who I was talking about and were impressed in spite of themselves.

We laughed, after he had gone, at the thought of there being anyone at the front who neither smoked nor drank, and read Homer in preference to anything else.

We could laugh, we had to laugh, there was laughter every

131

day because we were all young and there was no jealousy between us, and because laughter was the only way of survival on the Broenbeke.

Back on the Wijdendrift, A and B were having a worse time than ourselves. Casualties among officers had been particularly heavy. Jamieson had been gassed, Vernon wounded. Major Fraser also was suffering from the gas, he had lost his voice and could only speak in a whisper, he was coughing all the time. He ought to have gone into hospital, but he hung on, he said he would be all right in a day or two. But he had to go in the end, and he never came back to us. He lived for ten years after the war, but never wholly recovered from the gas and died in early middle age.

B Battery was so short of officers that we were ordered to send them one of ours until the arrival of reinforcements. I was dismayed when I heard that one of us was to go. I knew it would have to be Josh or myself, we were the two who had most recently come to the battery.

'Toss for it,' the Major said.

It had never occured to me that I might be sent away from my battery. I would rather have gone up to do an extra liaison, under all the Eyes in the Houthulst Forest. I certainly was not going to volunteer this time, however much Josh might want me to.

But Josh said 'I don't mind going. I don't mind where I go so long as there is a good roof on top of me. I like you all very much, even Frank, although he grouses about his mess bills, but one place is the same as another when you get to my age.'

'It will only be for a week or two,' the Major said.

It was only for one night. The roof was not a good one. A and B Battery officers were sharing a dug-out, and that night a gas shell came through the doorway and exploded inside,

132

and all its occupants were made casualties. One of them died a few days later. The other three were less seriously blistered by the liquid gas, but they were all taken to hospital, and the next news we had of them was that they were on their way to England.

We were all very sorry about Josh, for our own sakes if not for his.

'It's what he's been hoping for ever since he came out,' Frank said.

But Jack was not sure whether mustard gas was what he wanted. 'Some people say it prevents your having children,' he said. 'If you got it badly enough I suppose it might prevent your having anything else.'

'We shall miss him,' Frank said. 'Our whisky bills will be less, but we shall have no more roast chickens, it will be bully beef and maconochie from now on.'

I had never thought I should miss him so much, but the mess suddenly seemed empty without his big presence, his loud voice and his laughter.

The Major was angry. 'A gas shell!' he said. 'One gas shell! I ask you! They've been living there all this time, and they haven't made a place strong enough to keep out a gas shell. Well, they shan't have any more of my officers. They can do what they like with their own, but I won't give them any more of mine to squander. They can ask and go on asking, they can whistle themselves blue in the face, but they won't get any more from me.'

But they did not ask us to send anyone else. A and B were taken out of action, they had hardly any fit officers left. C and D stayed on.

I was less robust than some of the others, more likely to suffer from the cold and getting my clothes wet. I started coughing a lot and talked of going to see our doctor.

'How's your cough?' Jack asked me one evening.

'It's getting better,' I told him.

'Oh, bad luck!' he said sympathetically.

133

I had to do one more liaison duty, had to cross the wastes of death under the Watching Eyes once more.

There was an officer in D Battery called Percy White, brave and very capable. He had risen from the ranks, and been out continuously since Mons. I had heard his major say that he had done more than anyone else to hold the battery together during this difficult time. He came one morning to where I was standing by our guns and told me he had just come back from the worst twenty-four hours he had ever experienced in all his service.

'Talk about shell-fire!' he said. 'Sniping with machine-guns! Bodies! One of the pill-boxes was full of them. Smell of mustard gas all over the place. Mud and shell-holes everywhere.' He hoped he would never see the god-forsaken place again.

'Where is this place?' I asked. But I knew what he was going to say before he opened his mouth.

'U Six C Three Four,' he said.

'That's where I've got to go this afternoon,' I told him.

Before setting off I stopped at the bottom of the hill to speak to some of my men. They were far worse off than we were, living and sleeping (if they could sleep!) on the lip of a water-filled shell-hole, permanently wet and with only a few sandbags (if they were lucky!) to protect them from the flying splinters. There had been another infantry attack a day or two previously. It had achieved no more success than the one before, but we had fired hundreds of rounds of ammunition and the empty shell cases were useful for pinning down groundsheets on the least muddy parts of the swamp. Someone had brewed a pot of tea, and everyone within sight now had a mug in his hand. It was difficult to find wood, but Yorkshiremen were better than most at finding things and at improvisation. All the cooks were devoted men, somehow they supplied hot meals.

134

The infantry were in a worse plight than we were. Exposed to the bullet of a sniper whenever they moved, and with fewer hot meals. And still the battle went on. It was the ultimate in suffering. Gethsemane and the Broenbeke!

Sergeant Denmark was there, grousing as usual.

'If only we could feel we were doing some good to somebody,' I said to him.

'Reckon it may have done some to you,' he replied.

There seemed to be almost a note of approval in his voice.

We went on, my two signallers and I.

I was full of fear and foreboding as we left the world of men in the valley and went up the hill into the lonely wilderness, because of what White had told me.

But we were as fortunate as he had been the reverse. An easy journey up, unseen by the Eyes, a quiet night, friendly foot-sloggers when we arrived. It did not even rain, or less heavily than usual, and I managed to avoid seeing the pillbox where all the dead men were. And the next day I walked blithely down the hill, leaving the Houthulst Forest behind me. I never saw it again until the War was over when I went back to see whether it still had the power to inspire terror in me. My father was with me. He only saw a lot of shattered tree trunks and I did not tell him what else had been there once.

It was in early November that we escaped from the Broenbeke, and a day or two later we heard that Passchendaele had at last been captured. By the Canadians.

Passchendaele! There was a green hill far away, I had seen it with my own eyes just before the battle began, when Edward took me with him to the O.P. from the Summer House, in front of the Canal Bank. Far away! Neither of us could have guessed how far away it was on that sunny July day. And there was no city wall unless the pill-boxes were part of it. It had been a green hill when I first saw it, but now of course it was just black mud, like everything else.

The ultimate in suffering! But God had kept his promise

of salvation. Every material thing destroyed, but humankind and humanity had somehow survived. The suffering on the Broenbeke had probably been in vain, but not the suffering in the Garden.

16

Down South

Edward left us, to return to England and become a civilian again, a medical student instead of a soldier. During his last days with the battery he and the Major appeared to be vying with each other to see who could be most complimentary.

'We all owe our lives to him,' Edward said, 'you've only got to look at the other batteries and see what has happened to them. D have lost more than half their strength, A and B about half, but we've not lost more than a quarter of ours. It isn't only that he has a good eye for a gun position and finds a strong pill-box, he also stands up to the generals who want to bugger us about. They get no change out of Major Eric. He knows that keeping down casualties is the most important thing, and if he gets an order which he thinks will put lives at risk unnecessarily he just ignores it, no matter who it's come from.'

And the Major said to the rest of us 'Of course he's got to go, but it's a thousand pities. He's got the making of a really good officer and I would have recommended him for his majority when he'd had a little more experience. I've always known there was something special about him and I've always said so.'

It was a sad day for the battery when Edward went and he himself was the saddest person in it. He had spent a small fortune on cigarettes and beer for the men, and after breakfast on his last day he went out into the lines to say good-bye and shake hands with every man in the battery. I saw tears on his cheek when he came into the mess to say good-bye to us. 'I shall never find a place like this again,' he said, 'it's been like home to me.' Then he rode away to the station with his groom and some time later I saw Edric returning with the two horses. 'He has guts, that boy,' the Major said, 'and that's the only thing which matters when all's said and done.'

Only Frank could see a silver lining. Edward had escaped from the War. This was a miracle, and if one miracle could occur then there might be another and next time it might be he who escaped.

We were given a short rest before returning to the line, but we were not so happy as we had been in September. We were all of us worn out, the Broenbeke seemed to have taken away our power of finding any enjoyment.

Then we were ordered to entrain for an unknown destination, and for a day or two there was the excitement of mystery and playing a guessing game. This did not last. 'You're for Bapaume,' the Railway Transport Officer told us at the station, 'and unless you're quick you may find the Boche gets there before you.'

Strange things had been happening down south, on the Cambrai front, and were still happening. We had read about them in the newspaper. One of our armies had made a surprise attack, using tanks instead of artillery preparation which had the effect of warning the other side. The attack had been very successful, we had broken their line. But then the Germans had made a surprise counter-attack and had broken ours. They had been even more successful, they were still advancing. This was why the RTO said we should have to be quick.

We were quick. Our train averaged nearly twelve miles an hour instead of the usual eight or nine. But no one seemed in a hurry for us when we arrived at our journey's end, and we were kept waiting at the station for several hours. The Major was temporarily in command of the brigade, and he had gone on ahead, taking Frank with him to see the country before dark, and I was left to follow with the battery.

I did not know where to go and had to wait for orders. It was cold waiting. The sun had set, it was nearly dark before we set off. Le Transloy, Rocquigny, Manancourt—those were the names of the villages through which I was to pass. They had a pleasant sound after the harsher Flemish names. But

I had no map, and in the darkness it was not easy to find the way. The roads were deserted, and the villages, though easily recognisable as villages, were without inhabitants. This was part of the territory that had been given up by the Germans at the beginning of the year. They had made a voluntary retirement after blowing up all the houses and cutting down most of the trees.

The night was very cold. I walked most of the way, leading my horse behind me, because it was warmer to walk. The men had been singing at first, but the singing stopped long before we came to the end of our march, and then there was only the sound of the horses' feet and the wagon wheels behind me. I was tired and hungry as well as cold. At last I heard someone coming towards us. It was a guide who had come to lead us to the place where we were to spend the night.

'What sort of a place is it?' I asked.

'Just a field, sir,' he said.

The long wait at the station and the cold march had made me bad tempered, and the thought of camping in an open field added to my irritation. We had been living in huts while we were out at rest, and I hated the cold. But Frank, to whom I started grumbling as soon as I saw him, was unsympathetic. 'Don't you know there's a war on?' he said, and I felt ashamed of my outburst. What sort of a veteran was I if I could not endure a little cold weather! It had been shellfire and mud in Flanders, now it would be the hardship of winter that I should have to learn to bear.

But a hot meal was soon ready for us. The cooks were the most popular men in the battery that night. Then there was a double rum ration. Tents were pitched, my servant had laid everything out for me, I only had to climb inside my sleeping-bag, and then put all the clothes I had on top of it.

In the morning the ground was white with frost, but we had all slept well. The sun came up, and after breakfast I felt myself again, almost ready to enjoy whatever the day might bring. We rode out to look at the battery positions which we were to occupy. We were on that part of the front where the Germans had made their break-through, but their advance

139

had been halted before we arrived. The alarm was over, only a feeling of unease remained.

It seemed strange to be riding on horseback within two or three miles of the enemy. Everything was strange on that bright sunny morning: the hard dry ground, the absence of shell-holes and the sound of gunfire. Every now and then the silence was broken by the sound of a gun firing, but at Ypres the noise had been continuous.

We seemed to have the place to ourselves, our little party, two officers from each battery riding over the white deserted plain. It looked like a Christmas card, but there was no holly.

'We might be on Salisbury Plain,' Frank said, 'playing at being soldiers.'

Our first battery position was on the edge of a wood that was almost undamaged. We stayed there for three days without firing or being fired at. Then we were sent to another position a few miles away where we had some firing to do, and some shells came back at us. But it was very different from the Broenbeke.

'It's going to be rather serious,' Frank said, 'if either side in future can attack the other without warning.'

'It's not cricket,' the Major agreed.

He went with the Colonel and the other battery commanders to a conference of senior officers at which the lessons of the two recent battles were discussed.

'Trench warfare is a thing of the past,' he told us on his return. 'It's back to proper soldiering in future. No more of this mucking about in shell-holes and pill-boxes. The Brass Hats have always said it was wrong, and now Cambrai has proved them right. They say we shall enjoy it much more!'

'What exactly are we going to enjoy?' Jack asked.

'Oh, galloping about in the open, firing over open sights, saving the guns—all that sort of thing. We may all win Victoria Crosses.'

140

The Major was in his flippant mood, it was impossible to tell what had been said at the conference.

'You can't think how pleased the Staff are,' he said, 'at the idea of fighting properly again.'

'What about the Boche?' Frank asked. 'Has he agreed to the new rules?'

'Oh, I forgot to ask that one. I know there was a lot of talk about attacking.'

'Who's going to attack whom?'

'I think they said it would be Fritz's turn next.'

We were all to go in for winter training, the Major said, and the generals themselves were coming to watch us.

Jack said that he did not like change. 'I don't know the first thing about open warfare,' he said. 'It will be a funny thing if we start wishing ourselves back at Ypres.'

Winter training began at once. The guns had been brought out of action, but we were only a few miles behind the line, in readiness to go back immediately in the event of another attack. The Major was enthusiastic for the first few days. He enjoyed riding about on the downland in the bright winter sunshine with all the battery behind him, giving orders that none of us knew how to execute, and amused at the resulting confusion. 'We shall give the generals a surprise,' he said.

Jack was very worried. 'I haven't a clue as to what I'm supposed to do,' he said to me. 'It was all right up at Ypres, we just sat in a pill-box all day and went up to the O.P. when it was our turn.'

We all agreed that fighting in this part of the world would be very different from what it had been in Flanders and we wondered what 1918 would have in store for us.

'It may be better than 1917,' Frank said. 'At any rate we shan't have that gluey mud.'

'We shall have something else instead,' Jack said. 'It's more likely to be worse.' 'They did things better in the old days,' he went on, 'they used to go into winter quarters and no one had to sleep alone. I haven't seen a woman since September, except some I saw from the train working in the fields.'

'You're lucky,' he said to me, 'you seem able to get along without them.'

I could not get along without them. I wanted Suzanne more than ever and imagined myself with her every night as I was getting into my narrow sleeping-bag. Now she was smiling again, as friendly as she had been at first, talking to me about myself, wanting to console me for the suffering she saw in my eyes. She looked more beautiful than ever. My imagination made me very happy.

17

Year's End

1917 was drawing to its unregretted end. The dry frosty
weather had given way to rain and the night bombers were
flying over the wagon lines area. Everyone felt in need of
jollification, but Christmas gave us very little. Peace and Good-
will were conspicuously absent, as were the shepherds and
their flocks. There were a lot of magpies, but no other living
creatures in this desolate land from which the Germans had
retired after completely destroying it. There was no girl nearer
than Amiens, fifteen miles away, Jack told us, and no
possibility of getting there. 'It's a bloody awful war,' he said,
and everyone agreed with him.

The Major decided to give a party on New Year's Eve, and
he invited Major Cecil, Garnett and two or three others. 'We'll
show them what C Battery can do,' he said, and he told the
servants to polish glasses and brass shell cases for candlesticks. They even contrived to make paper decorations for
the drab little hut that was our mess.

The party was a great success, and no one enjoyed it more
than the Major. For some days past he had been very
depressed, he was missing so many of his friends in the other
batteries. But the party made him a different man, tolerant,
light-hearted, as eager as a schoolboy for fun and games.
The weather had changed again, there had been a fall of snow
on the previous day, and when dinner was over he suggested
a snowball fight. Soon there were snowballs flying in every
direction, most of them aimed at the Major. All the servants
joined in the fight and they also combined against him, he
was the most popular officer in the battery. But being an
artillery major he knew the importance of having a good

supply of ammunition and I think he must have made a pile of snowballs before the game started, for he was giving as good as he got.

It was a dangerous game, for the snowfall had not been a heavy one and the snowballs were mixed with bits of chalk and stone. Besides, we had dug narrow trenches outside our huts in which to take refuge when the night flyers came over and we heard bombs dropping. We had not had to use them yet, but now I fell into one when I was running away from somebody. For a moment I thought I had broken my leg, but getting out I found I could walk. Then I realised I had drunk too much champagne, I was not accustomed to drinking. I went into our hut and lay down. I shut my eyes and kept still, hoping the sickness would pass. But it was no good, I should have to go out again and get rid of it. Fortunately I was able to avoid the others. They were making so much noise that it was easy to keep out of their way. I went away from the camp and was very sick. I felt better at once and half thought of going to join in the fun again; but I decided not to. I'd had enough, it was getting late, I did not want to fall into another trench. Next time I might break a leg, and that would be a poor way out.

I did not want any way out, I wanted to stay where I was. For as long as the war lasted this was where I belonged. At first I had just been an individual, now I was part of the battery, the battery was part of the brigade, and the brigade was part of the B.E.F. All my friends were in France, and all the men in France were my friends.

All the men in France! I had no enemies, or only the Staff, and they lived so far away that we did not think of them as part of us. Life was very simple at the front, you just served.

Now I was accepted. Everyone in the battery accepted me. At the beginning I had not been accepted because I knew nothing about war and nothing about life. I knew all about war now, everyone said the Broenbeke was as bad as anything there had ever been. I had not learnt much more about life. Major Fraser had offered me a chance of learning, but I had turned it down and did not regret doing so. Knowledge of the war had come to me simply and naturally, I had not gone out of my way to look for Bank Farm or the Eyes of the Houthulst Forest. I believed knowledge of life would come in the same simple and natural way when I was ready for it. There was a big picture of a naked woman on the wall of the mess, left there by the hut's last occupant. I loved looking at her breasts and beautiful long legs. One day it would not be just a picture I was looking at. She, my girl, would be in bed beside me, I should be kissing her breasts, running my hands along the silkiness of her thighs, finding the wonder between them.

The light touch of Suzanne's hair against my cheek had set my heart on fire. But there was more than that to come, more even than kissing. I had not succeeded in kissing Suzanne, but that was because of the language barrier. A girl wanted to be told that she was beautiful, that you adored her and needed her more than anything else in the world. I could not say any of these things to Suzanne because of my bad French, but I should say them all to my English girl when I found her. Words could be very persuasive. And then the ecstasy of passion! That was what Jack called it, and I knew Frank was looking forward to it as the supreme moment of life.

The ecstasy of passion! It would be as momentous, as unforgettable as coming under fire for the first time. That night at Neuve Église and the nights spent with the working party at Gibraltar Farm had changed me into a different person. There would come another night that would change me again. The first change had been as frightening as it was thrilling, but the second would be altogether wonderful.

I was still thinking about Suzanne's beauty when I heard the voices of the others outside. The snowballing was over, the guests had gone, now Frank and Jack were coming in. We three slept in one part of the hut, the Major had a small room of his own, leading out of ours. They came in, walked unsteadily across the hut, and sat down on my bed.

'Hello!' Frank said. 'Where did you go off to? What have you been doing?'

'Just thinking,' I told him.

'I feel bloody awful,' Jack said, 'it's all this mixing of drinks.

I told the Major I wanted to stick to whisky, but he kept filling my glass with bubbly when I wasn't looking.'

'And you kept emptying it,' Frank said.

'Well, you've got to be matey at a party.'

Now the Major had gone into his little room, and we heard him singing in his tuneless voice behind the thin partition.

'Old soldiers never die,
Never die, never die,
Old soldiers never die,
They simply fade away.'

'He sounds cheerful,' Frank said.

'Wonder how long it will last,' said Jack.

I wanted to be alone with my thoughts and was not sorry when they got up, went across to their own beds and started to undress. Presently I heard them discussing the war. Jack was saying he could not stick it much longer. Frank told him he would have to. 'We stuck it on the Somme,' he said, 'and we stuck it on the Broenbeke. We can stick it as long as we've got to.'

'But you've got to admit it's a hopeless dawn.'

Then Frank looked at his watch. 'It's long after midnight, he said. 'Happy New Year to us all!'

'Don't be so bloody sarcastic,' Jack said.

The singing next door had stopped and, one by one, we fell asleep.